plants of
eden

by Louise Frost and Alistair Griffiths
Foreword by Philip McMillan Browse

Alison Hodge

contents

foreword

by Philip McMillan Browse

Director of Horticulture, Eden Project

The essential element of the Eden Project's *raison d'être* is 'man's relationship with plants'. This concept encompasses and bridges the need for the conservation of plants in wild places and the exploitation of plants, by humans, at whatever level.

'Exploitation' has many meanings, but here it implies, in its simplest sense, the growing and using of plants for food, fuel, building, medicines and so on – not forgetting the aesthetic pleasures gained from their floral beauty, scent and form; right through the spectrum to monocultural agronomic practices. Conservation refers to the need for the maintenance of biodiversity and the survival of plant species in the wild; and hence to an awareness and acknowledgement of the current pressures created by increasing development and population.

Eden seeks to assist in the process of understanding this dilemma, and to provide an opportunity for real, effective and even-handed action in the resolution of the inevitable conflicts that arise.

The 30 plants illustrated and described in the following pages are a first representation of the diversity of plants growing at Eden. They are chosen from the three biomes that we currently have – and ten from each of these are presented.

These plants were selected – almost at random – to demonstrate the range of stories and interest that accompany plants in any situation, and how humans have impacted on them for their own benefit.

It is a privilege to acknowledge that this book has been written by two of our younger members of staff and thus, I am confident, demonstrates the strengths, commitment and integration of the Eden team.

April 2001

3

Angel's trumpet – *Brugmansia* – are perennial shrubs or trees, which grow to a height of about 11 m. (36 ft.). Their fluted, pendulous flowers open for four to six days, and can reach 40 cm. (16 in.) in length. This is true of *Brugmansia* 'Charles Grimaldi' (1), which is a cultivar. All species are strongly scented, with only *B. sanguinea* lacking scent.

There are some five species in the genus *Brugmansia*, and many hybrids and cultivars. All were formerly included in the genus *Datura*, which now includes only the herbaceous, or sub-shrub species with upright flowers.

Brugmansia grow easily in gardens without frost, and in the south-west of England they can bloom for most of the year. The hardiest species is *B. sanguinea*. Even after light frosts the plant will sprout again in the spring, after pruning.

Certain species of *Brugmansia* have been grown in British gardens for centuries. The first references to them date from the mid 16th century, and it is probable that they were introduced here soon after the European discovery of America. They originated in the Andes, where they occur naturally in scrubland and beside streams. Humans and *Brugmansia* have had a long association, and often *Brugmansia* growing in the wild is evidence of a previous habitation.

Apart from their floral beauty, *Brugmansia* are grown for their medicinal and narcotic properties, mainly at lower elevations in Central and South America. *Brugmansia* contain powerful alkaloids, which produce strong physiological effects on the body. The two main alkaloids are hyoscyamine and scopolamine, which are used extensively in Western medicine. Hyoscyamine – commonly known as atropine – is used to treat spasms in skeletal muscles; as an antispasmodic in the treatment of asthma, and as an antidote to nerve gas and certain insecticides. The species *B. arborea* contains high levels of hyoscyamine, and its flowers are used to induce clairvoyance!

Scopolamine occurs in all plants of the Solanaceae – potato – family. It is similar to hyoscyamine, but acts as a central nervous system depressant, making it valuable as a sedative and as a pre-anaesthetic. It is also used medically to dilate the eyes. However, its current main use is for the prevention of motion sickness, and it is often applied as a skin patch behind the ear.

In many countries where traditional medicine is practised, it is believed that the spirit world inflicts illness, and that a person is cured by restoring the balance of body and mind. Manipulation of the spirit world alongside the use of plant-derived medicines is very widely practised, and many different plants are involved. For example, in Ecuador bunches of medicinal plants, including *Brugmansia*, are brushed against a sick person to transfer harm from the sufferer, and to give some protection for the future.

Hallucinogenic uses of *Brugmansia* are common among the peoples of Central and South America. The drug is made from the dried leaves, sometimes mixed with the flowers, and sometimes with the fruits. The leaves are rolled, wrinkled, or broken, and have a disagreeable odour and a slightly nauseous, bitter taste. Traditionally, the drug was used only by village elders in certain ceremonies. In fact, it is highly toxic, and very dangerous as an experimental drug. Many young people in South America have become victim to its effects.

The Eden Project has many large *Brugmansia* species, displayed in the Floral Beauty exhibit.

The beautiful, exotic-looking angel's trumpet is in fact a member of the potato family, Solanaceae!

angel's trumpet

1. *Brugmansia* 'Charles Grimaldi'.
2. *Brugmansia* growing wild in Jamaica.
3. This mosaic shows why angel's trumpet got its name.

Alexander the Great, and Oliver Cromwell - just two of the famous people killed by malaria, or the ague, as it used to be called.

Malaria was once a world-wide health problem, and for hundreds of years the only cure was quinine - an alkaloid found in the bark of *Cinchona*.

Cinchona belongs to the madder family - Rubiaceae. It is an ever-green tree or shrub, of the genus *Cinchona*, that is native to South America - especially Peru. There are many species of *Cinchona*, but only a few have been useful in treating malaria. The trees with the highest yielding barks originated in northern Bolivia and adjacent Peru.

Cinchona bark is harvested by uprooting the trees at about 12 years of age, and stripping the raw material from both stems and roots. Sometimes, only the trunk is used, and the stump is allowed to regenerate.

The Quechua Indians used *Cinchona* bark as a medicine long before the Spanish conquests of the 16th century. The Jesuit fathers found that it cured malaria, and named it 'Jesuits' powder'. From 1651 to 1660, they monopolised its commercial use. But the Jesuits were widely hated and feared in Europe, and were not taken seriously, despite their attempts to convince people that they had found a miracle cure.

At this time, England was rife with malaria, and an Englishman, Robert Talbot, found a cure. He cured King Charles II; King Louis XIV of France, and the Queen of Spain, and was knighted for his efforts. Throughout his life, Talbot kept his secret, and warned people about the dangers of using Jesuits' powder. Eventually, he divulged his secret recipe to Louis XIV, who revealed it only after Talbot's death. Talbot died a rich man in 1681, and King Louis let it be known that

Talbot's secret cure was none other than Jesuits' powder!

By the end of the 17th century, *Cinchona* bark was a world-wide remedy for malaria. Huge shipments from Peru and Bolivia, and the continued exploitation of wild trees, caused scarcity, and in the 19th century efforts were made to cultivate *Cinchona* in other parts of the world, in order to break the Spanish monopoly. The Dutch in Java, and the British in India and Ceylon (Sri Lanka) attempted to start their own monopolies of quinine. Millions of trees were shipped to these countries and cultured, and large amounts of money and time were wasted on species that yielded very little quinine.

Eventually, the Andean quinine monopoly came to an end through the actions of an English trader, Charles Ledger, who lived on the shores of Lake Titicaca, in Bolivia. In 1865, Ledger sent the seeds of a plant with high quinine content, yielding between 10 and 13 per cent, to his brother in England, to sell to the British Empire's Indian plantations. The Government refused to buy them, so some of the seeds were sold to the Dutch for their Java plantations. This high-yielding species was later named after Ledger, as *Cinchona*

ledgeriana. The plant was rather slow growing, and subject to disease, especially at the seedling stage. But the Dutch overcame these problems by grafting it on to stronger root stock, and by 1884, Java took over the quinine bark trade from South America. The Dutch Government had a virtual monopoly of supply until Java fell to the Japanese in the Second World War.

In 1944, the artificial synthesis of alkaloids chemically similar to quinine - atabrine, chloroquinine and primaquine, for example - reduced the need for natural quinine, and for many years all anti-malarial drugs have been produced synthetically. Recently, however, some strains of malaria have become resistant to many of the synthetic chemicals, and there is a revived interest in natural quinine, which seems to be effective against these strains.

Today, quinine remains a viable commercial product because of its other uses in medicines, mouthwashes, and beverages such as tonic water.

Cinchona species contain 30 alkaloids, of which the most useful is quinine. Quinidine - another useful compound - is used in the treatment of heart disease.

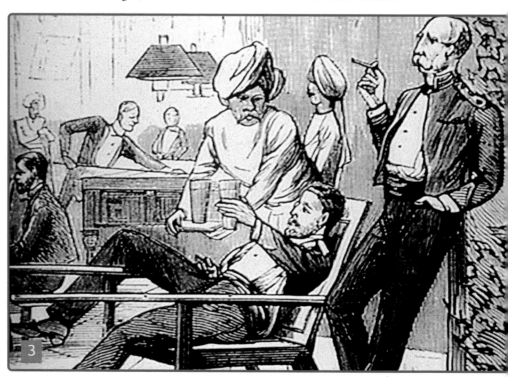

cinchona

The Quechua Indian name for *Cinchona* was *quina*, meaning 'bark'. Later, it was called *quina quina* – 'bark of barks' – hence quinine.

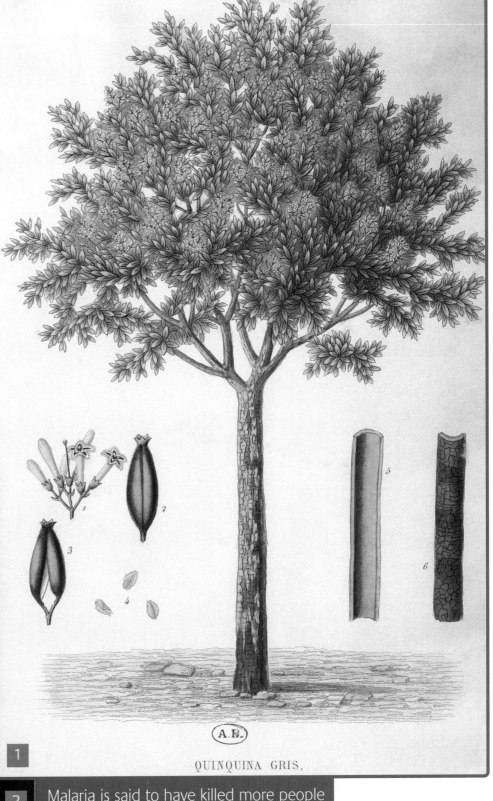

QUINQUINA GRIS.

1

2 Malaria is said to have killed more people than all the wars and plagues together.

1. A 19th-century French botanical print of the Grey *Cinchona*.

2. The bark of a *Cinchona* sapling being stripped to produce quinine.

3. An old print illustrating the early use of 'tonic water' in colonial India.

Coffee, which helps many of us survive early mornings and long nights, is second only to petroleum as a globally traded commodity. Around 25 million people rely on its production for their livelihood.

We do not know exactly where or when coffee was first cultivated, but some authorities believe it was in Arabia, near the Red Sea, c. AD 675. The wild types of coffee, now under threat, grow today in Ethiopia's montane forest.

One legend attributes the discovery of coffee to an Ethiopian herdsman, who noticed his goats were unusually frisky after eating coffee berries. After this, people started eating them, mainly for their stimulating properties.

Coffee cultivation was rare until the 15th and 16th centuries, when extensive planting of trees occurred in the Yemen region of Arabia. The Arabs were the first people to brew coffee as we know it.

Coffee consumption increased in Europe during the 17th century, and it was soon a popular drink in Britain. By 1675 there were more than 3,000 coffee houses in London alone. They became important places for debate and gossip.

In 1714, the French brought a live cutting of a coffee tree to the island of Martinique in the Caribbean. This single plant was the genesis of the great coffee plantations of Latin America.

Today, Brazil and Colombia are the two biggest coffee exporters; Brazil produces about a quarter of the world's supply. Coffee is also grown on the islands of Java and Sumatra (Indonesia), and in Arabia, India, Africa and the Caribbean.

Annual coffee production today is about 6.4 million tonnes of green beans. Coffee is harvested from seeds of different species, but only three are commercially important: Arabian, robusta and Liberian. Arabian coffee is classified as *Coffea arabica*, robusta as *Coffea canephora*, and Liberian as *Coffea liberica*. These tropical ever-

More than 400 billion cups of coffee are consumed every year, making it the world's most popular drink after water.

green shrubs or small trees – 4.6 to 6 m. (15–20 ft.) high at maturity – bear shiny, green, ovate leaves and white, fragrant flowers that bloom for only a few days.

During the six or seven months after flowering, the fruit develops, growing in clusters and changing from light green to red, and ultimately to deep crimson. The mature fruit resembles a cherry and usually contains two seeds, or beans.

The coffee tree produces its first full crop at about five years old; thereafter it produces consistently for 15 to 20 years. One tree can yield 0.9–1.3 kg. (2–3 lb.) of marketable green beans annually.

Several varieties of green coffee are usually blended and roasted together to produce the aromas and flavours popular with coffee lovers.

The beans are heated in rotating, horizontal drums, at temperatures of up to 218°C (424°F). Roasting affects some of the chemicals in the beans – particularly those that are responsible for the aroma.

The principal stimulatory effects of coffee are due to the presence of the alkaloid caffeine. In recent years, caffeine has been identified as a possible cause of cancer and of birth defects, but such suggestions remain unconfirmed. The main physiological effects of caffeine are increased blood pressure; stimulation of the central nervous system; the promotion of urine formation, and the stimulation of heart and lung activity.

Caffeine is used in treating migraine because it constricts the dilated blood vessels, thus reducing the pain. It increases the potency of analgesics such as aspirin, and it can relieve asthma attacks by widening the bronchial airways.

Our exhibit shows how coffee is grown, harvested and processed.

coffee

Coffee is so widely grown that if all the coffee plantations were placed together, they would form a solid band 1.6 km. (1 mile) wide around the Equator.

1. Coffee bushes, shaded by banana plants, growing high in Jamaica's Blue Mountains.

2. Ripe coffee berries.

3. Picking coffee berries in Thailand. Coffee is often grown on mountain slopes, and the berries do not all ripen at the same time, so they are generally picked by hand.

4. When the outer husk has been crushed off, the beans are spread out in the sun to dry.

5. Roasted coffee beans.

Without papyrus, many important scrolls of ancient Egypt, and the works of some of the great Greek and Roman scholars might never have been written. For papyrus – *Cyperus papyrus* – was the main writing material of classical antiquity. Indeed, 'papyrus' means paper, and the plant was used primarily to make this paper-like substance.

Cyperus papyrus (papyrus, paper plant) belongs to the *Cyperaceae* family, which consists of 4,000 species. It is an elegant sedge that grows naturally in Central Africa and the Nile valley, and is naturalised in Sicily. It grows up to 4.6 m. (15 ft.) high in slow-flowing water. The smooth, triangular stems, which are characteristic of sedges, can have the diameter of a small child's arm.

Egyptian papyrus scrolls have been found dating back to 2800 BC.

The flowers appearing at the end of these stems resemble huge, rounded domes.

Papyrus was an important resource for the ancient Egyptians. In addition to paper, it provided food, heating and clothing. The pith of the stem was boiled and eaten. The roots were dried and used for heating and cooking. The stem was used in the manufacture of clothes, sails, mats, cords and ornamental boxes. Papyrus twisted with alfalfa grass, date-palm fibre and camel hair made the ropes for an extensive range of majestic barges, boats and warships. The people of Lakes Tana and Awasa in Ethiopia,

and Lake Titicaca in the Andes, still use papyrus plants to make boats for use on the lakes.

To produce paper from this plant was a laborious process. First, papyrus stems were collected. Then the central pith was cut into thin strips and laid lengthways, with further layers placed crosswise on top. The whole sheet was moistened with water, pressed and dried. On drying in the sun, the plant's glue-like sap acted as an adhesive, cementing the layers together. The dried material was then hammered to make it more compact, and rubbed with ivory, stone or bone to produce a smooth surface. Several of these flat sheets were stuck together to make a scroll – some scrolls reaching as much as 6–9 m. (20–30 ft.) in length.

Papyrus was cultivated and used for writing by the Arabs of Egypt, until the growing manufacture of paper from other plant fibres in the 8th and 9th centuries AD rendered it unnecessary. By the 3rd century AD, papyrus was already being replaced by vellum, or parchment made of animal skins, which was less expensive. But the use of papyrus for books and documents persisted sporadically until about the 12th century, when rag and wood pulp paper took over. Today, the art of making paper from papyrus continues for the tourist trade in Egypt.

In temperate climates, papyrus is grown as an exotic, ornamental aquatic plant in hothouses. It is readily propagated by division and seed, and thrives in high temperatures and high humidity. A close relative – *Cyperus involucratus* (Umbrella plant) – makes an unusual, but elegant houseplant.

At the Eden Project, you can follow the paper trail of plants used to make paper from throughout the world.

1. Papyrus growing in Egypt.
2. Fishing from a papyrus raft, Lake Awasa, Ethiopia.
3. Ancient Egyptian illustration on papyrus.

papyrus

The legendary tropical passion-flower – *Passiflora* – is one of the most spectacular and attractive flowering plants in the world. It provides us with edible fruits, used in foods, drinks and medicines; and is also used in poisons!

Early Spanish missionaries in South America identified an unusual parallel between these plants and potent Christian symbolism. They believed that the flowers represented the Crucifixion of Christ. The corona of the flower represented the crown of thorns, twisted and plaited; the five anthers, the five wounds received by Jesus on the cross; the three styles, the three nails; the five sepals and five petals, the apostles – minus Peter and Judas; the hand-like leaves and tendrils, the hands and scourges of Christ's persecutors. There are many variations of this legend, and it is thought that a European version was based on *Passiflora caerulea*, the hardiest and most widely cultivated passion-flower in the UK.

There are over 460 species of *Passiflora*, distributed in tropical and subtropical regions, chiefly in America and Africa. Between 50 and 60 of these species have edible fruits, but only five are used commercially. They produce thousands of tonnes of fruit per annum, which is eaten fresh or as a vegetable, or is processed into drinks, sweets and sherbets, or included in various desserts. *P. edulis* – a native of southern Brazil and Argentina – is the most widely cultivated passion-flower, and is grown for its fruits: it yields 23,000–40,000 kg. per ha. (20,000–35,000 lb. per a.) of crop. Other important commercial fruit-bearing passion-flowers are *P. laurifolia, P. ligularis, P. mollissima* and *P. quadrangularis*.

In South America, *P. holosericea* and *P. mexicana* are used as tea. In the USA, *P. foetida* root is used as an antispasmodic; and in Europe, herbalists use *P. incarnata* for the same purpose, in the treatment of Parkinson's disease. The dried foliage of some species contains an alkaloid poison, which is used as a mild sedative. The seeds of *P. coriacea* are used as an insecticide, and the leaves of *P. pulchella* have diuretic properties.

The hybrid *P. x decaisneana*, which is grown in hothouses in temperate countries, is commonly mislabelled in plant collections as *P. quadrangularis* (a parent of this hybrid). *P. quadrangularis* – the Giant Granadilla – is a plant with one of the largest tropical fruits. It has a thick, aromatic rind, and can reach the size of a water-melon. Most parts of this plant have been used medically at some time.

The raw root is said to be a narcotic, but is used as an emetic, diuretic and vermifuge. Powdered and mixed with oil, it makes a soothing poultice, as do the leaves, which are used to treat liver complaints. The fruit is used as an antiscorbutic and stomachic in the tropics, and in Brazil the rind is prescribed for the relief of asthma, headaches, diarrhoea, dysentery, neurasthenia and insomnia.

Passion-flowers also have a remarkable relationship with over 70 species of tropical butterflies of the subfamily *Heliconiinae* – the passion-flower butterflies. Over thousands of years, a great evolutionary battle has been fought between plants and butterflies. It is thought that the plants have adapted to protect themselves from being devoured by the caterpillars, while at the same time creating the right environment to ensure pollination by the adults. The plants have evolved disguises, by changing leaf shape; pumping poisons into their leaves; creating homes for caterpillar-attacking ants, and even developing mimics of butterfly eggs on their leaf stalks to deter egg-laying females!

1. *Passiflora x decaisneana*.
2. *Passiflora caerulea*.
3. The fruit of *Passiflora edulis* – the most widely cultivated passion-flower.

passion-

1

flower

Of the many food plants introduced to Europe from America, few, if any, created more interest than the pineapple. When Christopher Columbus reached the Caribbean, pineapple cultivation had already spread there from Brazil. It is said that Columbus was astonished and delighted by the fruit's qualities, and by its similarities to pine-cones – hence the common English name.

There are eight species of pineapples – classified as *Ananas* – which belong to the family Bromeliaceae. The name *Ananas* comes from the Brazilian Tupi Indian word meaning 'excellent fruit'. Today, *Ananas comosus* 'Cayenne' and *A. comosus* 'Queen' are the main crop varieties.

Pineapples are evergreen biennials or perennials, growing to about 1 m. (3 ft.) high. They have adapted to drought conditions with short stems, and expanded leaf stalks, which grow to form a water-holding tank at the base of the plant. Water is absorbed from the tank as needed by roots and leaf hairs. The famous fruit is a composite structure of 100–200 berry-like fruitlets, fused together and producing a tessellated appearance. Fruits average about 15 cm. (6 in.) long, and weigh between 1 and 2 kg. (2–4 lb.). Giant Kew varieties can reach 10 kg. (22 lb.)!

By the 1520s, European gardeners were growing pineapples from plant material brought to Spain. In 1661, John Rose – one of Charles II's gardeners – grew the first English pineapple. Victorian gardeners developed the cultivation of pineapples into a fine art, but interest faded when pineapples arrived in Britain from the Azores: the short journey allowed the fruits to arrive fresh.

Pineapple cultivation spread quickly throughout the tropics. By the mid 16th century, the fruit was grown in India, Java and China. In the early 19th century, it was introduced to Hawaii, and with the encouragement of a young American entrepreneur – J.D. Dole – pineapple production became big business. In 1892, pineapple canning began in Hawaii, and in Malaya/Singapore. From then on, production rose dramatically, creating employment and money for many people in the tropics.

Today, total annual global production of pineapples is about 13 million tonnes. Hawaiian plantations produce almost one-third of the world's crop, and supply 60 per

The pineapple has long been considered a symbol of hospitality. In 18th-century England, stone pineapples were placed on gateposts, along drives, and over doors.

1. *Ananas comosus.* The fruit is a composite of 100–200 berry-like fruitlets, fused together.

2 and 3. Pineapples are a field crop in many tropical countries.

cent of canned pineapple products. Other leading producers are Malaysia, China, Brazil, and Mexico.

In Brazil and Paraguay, the Guarani Indians – who were probably the first people to cultivate pineapples – drank the juice to aid digestion after eating meat, and as a cure for stomach-ache. It was also used to promote the healing of wounds; to make an alcoholic beverage, and as a component of arrow poison. The Philippines has a long history of cloth production from pineapple-leaf fibres. Most of the fibres are still woven by hand: a skilled weaver can produce 1 m. (3 ft.) of cloth in a day – from about 60 fresh leaves.

In recent years, new uses of the pineapple have been discovered. The fruit contains the enzyme bromelin, which degrades protein. This has been shown to break down proteins such as fibrin, which is responsible for blockages in blood vessels. Such properties make bromelin potentially useful in the treatment of heart attacks and strokes caused by the accretion of proteins in the blood vessels.

The Eden Project has different varieties of pineapples in a small plantation.

1

pineapple

Rice is the world's number one food crop: it feeds half the world's population. Some 2.5 billion people depend on rice as a large part of their daily diet and calorie intake. In much of Asia, people eat rice two or three times a day.

Rice is the common name for about 19 species of annual herbs, of the grass family Gramineae, and belongs to the genus *Oryza*. It is also classed as a cereal crop.

Rice was one of the first domesticated crops. It was probably cultivated in the Yangtse basin, in southern China, more than 9,000 years ago.

Common rice is classified as *Oryza sativa*. There are thought to be over 140,000 varieties of cultivated rice – developed to suit a wide diversity of climates and soil types.

Agriculturists group rice into four main types: upland rice, which is grown on hillsides; rain-fed rice, grown in shallow water; irrigated rice, grown in shallow water fed from storage and drainage systems, and not reliant on rain; and deep-water rice, grown in estuaries or other areas liable to flooding. Mainland China grows irrigated rice almost exclusively. Latin America grows about 75 per cent upland rice, and is the world's largest producer of this type – huge areas of rainforest have been cleared to grow the crop. South Asia grows around one-third rain-fed rice; the rest is irrigated.

Rice takes from 90 to 260 days to mature, depending on cultivar, climate and environmental conditions. It takes about 30 days from flowering to seed-ripening. When fully mature, some varieties reach a height of 5 m. (16 ft.), but 1 m. (3 ft.) is average. The grain is produced on a nodding panicle of spikelets at the top of the stalk.

Asia accounts for 90 per cent of the world's production and consumption of rice. The plant thrives in its hot, humid climate, and is grown mostly on tiny farms, primarily to meet family needs. The marketable surplus is small, and prices fluctuate widely with droughts, floods and typhoons.

Rice is cultivated extensively in parts of Africa, and South America. The USA, southern Europe, and other regions also contribute significantly to total world production.

In the developing world, rice cultivation is largely unmechanised. Seedlings are grown in nurseries, and transplanted plant by plant into fields, so the rice plants have a head start over the weeds. Traditionally, almost all of the work is done by women.

In the USA, a flooded field, or paddy, is often sown with seed from an aeroplane. The field is kept flooded during most of the growing season, and the crop is harvested and threshed by a single machine. The main growing area is the Sacramento delta, in California.

Brown rice is dried and cleaned before it is packed. White rice is prepared by removing the bran, then polishing the rice kernels to enhance their appearance. The bran contains protein, and vitamins B complex, E, and K. White rice is therefore an inferior food to brown rice.

When the world switched from brown to polished rice, the loss of the bran and germ was a subtle dietary change with profound consequences. In the 19th century, thousands of people who had started eating white rice, experienced loss of muscle tone in the arms and legs. The disease was later diagnosed as 'beriberi' – caused by a lack of vitamin B_1. Recognition of the nutritional value of rice bran has led to an increase in the consumption of brown rice and, in

some areas, polished rice is sprayed with synthetic vitamin B_1.

In the 1960s, experiments by the International Rice Research Institute (IRRI) produced varieties of rice that doubled the world's rice harvest by the end of the 20th century. Researchers developed a short, vigorous rice, with a higher yield than traditional varieties. It was more easily harvested, and less likely to rot. These advances were termed the 'Green Revolution'. However, there has been criticism of the intensive agricultural methods adopted to achieve the high yields, which have caused social and environmental damage.

By 2020, there will be 1.2 billion new rice consumers in Asia – due to the growing population – and rice production must increase by one-third. The key to this will be achievements in plant breeding; the spread of irrigation, and the growth in the use of fertilisers.

The Eden Project's Malaysian area and Rice exhibit features different varieties of rice, and methods of cultivation and harvesting. It also shows the demands that the spiralling world population will have on rice production.

rice

Asia produces about 550 million tonnes of rice a year. It is grown over an area of nearly 150 million ha. (370 million a.), and accounts for half of Asia's farm incomes.

1. Common rice – *Oryza sativa* – is a member of the grass family, Gramineae.

2. Planting out rice seedlings in a vast flooded field in Florida, USA.

3. Much rice is grown on terraced hillsides in Asia.

Gumboots, tyres and erasers – these are just a few of the rubber products we use, and take for granted, every day.

Rubber-like substances are produced from more than 2,000 plant species, but 90 per cent of the world's rubber is obtained from only one plant – *Hevea brasiliensis* – the Para rubber tree.

Para rubber is a member of the large and diverse spurge family – Euphorbiaceae – and is native to the Amazon region. It is a quick-growing, erect, tropical tree that can reach heights of up to 40 m. (130 ft.) and girths of 2.6–3.3 m. (8–11ft.). Its stem is typically smooth and straight, with a much-branched, leafy canopy, greyish bark, and leaves of three leaflets.

Para rubber is prized for its latex-producing inner bark. Latex is a milky sap, like that found in dandelions, which is produced by many plants. It is produced in the inner bark of many tropical trees, including para rubber, in special cells called lactifers. Latex is thought to act as a natural defence mechanism against predatory insects, by gumming their mouth parts, and poisoning or repelling them with poisonous compounds.

Para rubber becomes tappable at seven years old. Tapping is a skilled job, as the bark must be cut at the right depth to sever the lactifers, without going through the inner bark and damaging the tree. Special tapping knives are used to make a cut from high left to low right, at an angle of 30°, and a thin shaving is taken off. When the cut is fresh, the latex flows to the lower end, where it is conducted by means of a small spout to a cup held on a hanger. The latex is dried in the sun before being sent to rubber-manufacturing industries.

We know that rubber was in use in the Caribbean and Central and South America by the late 15th century, to make balls, shoes, containers and coat fabrics. In 1823,

a Scotsman, Charles Macintosh, coated cloth with rubber, and invented the Macintosh raincoat. In 1839, a US inventor, Charles Goodyear, from New Haven, Connecticut, made the greatest discovery about rubber. He invented the vulcanisation process, by which rubber is stabilised by heating it with sulphur. This led to many new uses of rubber, including the manufacture of tyres. It was a Scottish engineer, John Dunlop, who patented the bicycle tyre in 1888.

In 1872, Joseph Hooker, Director of the Royal Botanic Gardens, Kew, sent Henry Alexander Wickham to Brazil to obtain rubber seeds. Wickham shipped 70,000 seeds to Kew. But rubber seeds do not remain viable for long, and only 9,000 germinated.

The seedlings were shipped in portable greenhouses to Ceylon (Sri Lanka), and from there to Singapore. Only a few survived, but they were the basis of today's rubber plantations in South-East Asia. Rubber was soon in great demand, and latex was often called white gold.

Today, there is still a huge demand for natural rubber, and although there are many synthetic rubbers, it accounts for about 30 per cent of the world's rubber consumption. It is thought that natural rubber will increase in importance as petroleum reserves diminish.

One day, you will be able to see how rubber is tapped from *Hevea brasiliensis* in the Eden Project's small plantation.

4

Rubber was named by an 18th-century British scientist, Joseph Priestley, when he found it would rub out – or erase – his pencil scribbles.

1. Cutting the bark of *Hevea brasiliensis* to sever the lactifers.
2. Latex is collected in a small cup.
3. Raw rubber in a wholesale store.
4. This diving suit is one of many products made from rubber.

rubber

A tapper harvests about 450 trees a day. Para rubber is grown over more than 7 million ha. (17 million a.), that produce about 6.5 million tonnes of natural rubber every year.

The vanilla plant – *Vanilla plani-folia* – belongs to one of the largest flowering plant families in the world – Orchidaceae, the orchid family. Of the thousands of orchid varieties, the vanilla plant is one of only a few to have edible properties. The others are *Barlia robertiana,* and species of *Eulophia, Dactylorhiza* and *Orchis.* Their tubers are used to make *salep*, a component of ice-cream, especially in the Mediterranean region.

Vanilla is a tropical, perennial, climbing vine, native to the humid, coastal rain forest of Mexico. It was introduced to Europeans in 1520, when offered by Montezuma – the last ruler of the Aztecs – to the conquistador Hernando Cortés, in a beverage called *chocolatl.* This brew was a delectable concoction of ground cacao and annatto seeds, chilli pepper and vanilla.

By the end of the 16th century, the Spaniards had established

factories to manufacture chocolate with vanilla flavouring, and for many years they controlled the production of vanilla.

In the early 1800s, vanilla was taken to Mauritius, giving rise to the vanilla industry around the Indian Ocean. Today, vanilla is also grown in the Bourbon Islands, Indonesia, Mexico and Tahiti.

Vanilla flavour is obtained from the vanilla bean. In America, the formation of the beans occurs naturally, due to pollination by native bees and hummingbirds. Elsewhere, these pollinators do not occur, so hand pollination ensures the formation of the beans. In commercial production, one worker pollinates well over 1,000 flowers per day.

The immature beans are harvested six to nine months after pollination, when yellowing at the base. They are laid out on woollen blankets in the sun, and then wrapped in the blankets so they start to ferment. They are stored

in metal-lined, airtight boxes, and the sweating, or curing process may continue for several months. In the final stage, vanilla essence is extracted in ethanol. Alternative methods include the use of warm-water scalding, and baking ovens.

The chemical that imparts the recognisable vanilla flavour to foods is called vanillin. It is also used to create delightful fragrances in perfumes, and in toothpaste.

The production of natural vanilla is very labour-intensive and expensive, so a cheaper imitation has been developed. This is manu-factured from clove oil, or from a breakdown product of lignin from a conifer. It has a similar flavour to vanilla, but cannot beat the original great taste that the vanilla orchid produces.

Recently, an American biotech-nological group has developed a method of obtaining vanilla by culturing vanilla plant cells. This is a very exciting discovery, but it could have a huge economic impact on the world's producers of natural vanilla, because the technology could drop the price of natural vanilla from US$2,400 to US$50 per kg. (2 lb.)

The production of vanilla flavour from the vanilla bean is very labour-intensive and time-consuming, making vanilla the second most expensive spice in the world, after saffron.

vanilla

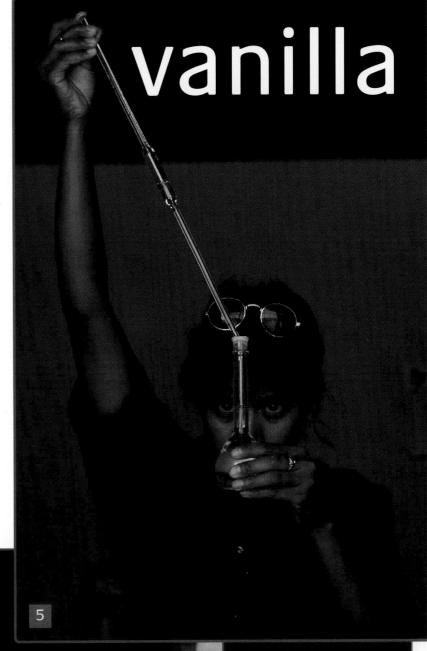

1, 2 & 3. *Vanilla planifolia* – buds, flower and bean – grown at the Eden Project's nursery. With the help of John Ledner, a member of the Mid-Cornwall Orchid Society, we have propagated vanilla by tip cuttings; grown them on; flowered them; hand-pollinated them, and produced beans.

4. Pods being checked and sorted in a vanilla processing plant, Madagascar.

5. Lab technician in Madagascar testing the quality of vanilla essence.

5

4

World consumption of vanilla beans is estimated at over 5.5 million tonnes a year. 1 ha. (2.5 a.) gives a yield of 500–800 cured pods a year over a crop life of about 7 years.

Yam is a tropical, edible crop, valued for its medicinal properties. Indeed, its importance in medicine is reflected in its scientific name *Dioscorea* – referring to Dioscorides, the classical Greek writer on medicine. Among its uses are the production of cortisone drugs, used in treating rheumatoid arthritis, asthma, hepatitis, leukemia and heart diseases.

Dioscorea belongs to a family of climbing tropical vines – Dioscoreaceae – native to South-East Asia, nearby Pacific islands, Africa, and South America. Yams contain plant steroids known as sapogenins, which are important medicinally. Diosogenin was discovered in the species *D. tokoro* in 1936, by two Japanese teams. However, it was the later research of an American, R.E. Marker, that enabled its commercial production for birth-control pills and cortisone drugs.

Yams tend to be starchy and bland to the taste, but they are rich in carbohydrates, proteins, amino acids, vitamins and minerals. In Fiji and other Pacific islands, and in many African countries, yams have long been a staple food source. Today, their primacy is challenged by the increase in cultivation of sweet potato and other tropical crops.

Yams are cooked and eaten in various ways, according to geographical location. Generally, they are peeled, then boiled, baked, fried, or sometimes roasted. A nutritious, glutinous dough called *foo foo* is popular in West Africa. It is prepared by boiling, and then vigorously pounding using a large pestle and mortar, to obtain the correct consistency. *Foo foo* is eaten with stews, and used in many other delightful dishes.

In Guyana, cultivars of *D. trifida* are used to prepare a beer called *kala*, or the *Wayapi's kalali*. In the Philippines, the most popular use of yams is in the making of ice-cream, jellies and yam-based candies.

Typically, edible yams have to be cooked before consumption to destroy a bitter, toxic substance called dioscorine. During periods of famine, highly toxic wild yams, such as *D. hispida* and *D. dumertorum*, are eaten. These take at least a week to prepare, before the toxin is reduced to safe levels. A traditional way of testing if the toxicity levels are safe for human consumption is to feed pieces of yam to chickens, and observe the results. Ironically, other species of yam are used in traditional animal feed, for wild and domesticated pigs.

To supplement diets, meat is obtained by using the toxic products from yams in hunting. *D. drageana, D. rupicola* and *D. piscatorium* are used for arrow poisons and bait. The alkaloids and saponins from these species have paralysing effects; they attack the red blood cells, and have been used to cull all kinds of animals, from the Himalayan tiger to small fish. They have also been used in human toxicology, as an ordeal poisoning; in criminal poisoning; and, more commonly, as a repellent in plots of cultivars.

The Eden Project's display features several different species of yam.

2

Yam extracts are used widely in the production of steroids for oral contraceptives and fertility drugs.

1. Yam plant, *Dioscorea bulbifera*.
2. A farmer harvests his yams, in south-east Nigeria.
3. Yams on the way to market.
4. Pounding yam with pestles and mortar, in Tanzania.

yam

The toxic properties of yams are used in insecticides. In Malaysia, *D. piscatorum* is used to protect rice from pests.

2

The traveller's palm belongs to the same family as the bird of paradise. It is so-called because water collects in the leaf bases, and quenches the thirst of travellers.

The bird of paradise is of no interest to ornithologists – yet it delights botanists, gardeners and plantsmen around the world!

The bird of paradise – *Strelitzia reginae* – is the most famous member of its family, Strelitziaceae. The group consists of from four to seven species, and is prized for its exotic flower. It is native to southern and eastern parts of Cape Province and northern Natal, South Africa, where it grows wild along riverbanks, and in scrub clearings in coastal areas. It is cultivated in both warm and cold temperate regions of the world as a garden plant, glasshouse ornamental, or houseplant.

Strelitzia reginae was introduced into cultivation in Britain in 1773, by Sir Joseph Banks, who named the plant in honour of Queen Charlotte, wife of George III, and Duchess of Mecklenburg-Strelitz. It obtained its common name – bird of paradise – because its flowers resemble the head of a brightly coloured tropical bird. It is a clump-forming, slow-growing, evergreen perennial that reaches 1.2 m. (4 ft.) in height, with greyish-green, oval leaves arising from an underground rhizome. Its exquisite blooms are rich purple, with vivid,

bright orange bracts that appear in a fan-like pattern. Flowering can occur all year round, but is mainly in spring and early summer.

In the wild, the bird of paradise is pollinated by the sunbird – *Nectarinia afra*. The bird lands on the flower, for the sweet nectar, and the flower's male organs lever clear of the rest of the flower, depositing pollen on the bird's breast. When the bird visits another flower, the pollen is transferred to the stigma – female organ – of the new flower, and pollination is completed.

In cultivation, hand pollination is necessary to produce seed. The seedpods contain from 60 to 80 seeds, which mature five months after pollination. However, in order to germinate, the seeds require bottom heat of at least 21°C (70°F). The plant is a very erratic germinator, and can take up to 18 months to germinate. Seedlings take from three to five years to produce flowers, whereas plants propagated by division flower in one or two years. Consequently, division is the favoured method of propagation.

The bird of paradise is used widely in subtropical countries in commercial horticulture. Its clump-forming habit provides the ideal bulk and mass for landscape planting. In temperate regions, it brings a warm, tropical feel to a large conservatory or house. Recently, the plant has become popular in the cut-flower industry – the cut flowers can last up to two weeks.

A delightful cultivar of *S. reginae* is 'Kirstenbosch Gold', named after Kirstenbosch National Botanical Garden, South Africa – one of the most famous botanical gardens in the world. *S. nicolai* is another noteworthy species, which was named after the Russian Emperor, Nicolas I. It has striking blue and white flowers, and reaches a towering height of 10 m. (33 ft.). It is seen widely in southern Spain.

At the Eden Project, *S. reginae* and *S. nicolai* are displayed in the Warm Temperate biome. Their close relatives – the traveller's palm, heliconias, bananas and gingers – are in the Humid Tropics biome.

bird of paradise

1

1. *Strelitzia reginae.*
2. Street seller, Santo Domingo,
   Dominican Republic.

Capsicum peppers – otherwise known as sweet or chilli peppers – are becoming increasingly popular in Britain. They are native to the Americas, and probably were first domesticated as hot peppers in Mexico, where seeds almost 5,000 years old have been found. It is said that Christopher Columbus discovered the fruit in the Caribbean, and named it pepper after mistaking it for the plant that produces black pepper.

Today, capsicum peppers are cultivated commercially throughout the tropical and subtropical regions of the world, with the main producers in Central and South America, the Far East, and East and West Africa.

Peppers are perennial sub-shrubs, but are usually grown as annuals in temperate zones. They are closely related to tomatoes, potatoes and eggplants – all of them being members of the family Solanaceae. Varieties of capsicum peppers vary in length from about 2.5 cm. (1 in.) to 20 cm. (8 in.), and range in colour from green to orange, red, yellow and purple. Five species are generally recognised: *C. annuum*, *C. frutescens*, *C. baccatum*, *C. pubescens* and *C. chinense*. In addition, there are between 2,000 and 3,000 varieties of capsicums. These include anaheim, banana, cayenne, chiltecpin, habernero, jalapeno, peri peri, pimento, poblano, scotch bonnet, and serrano.

Capsicum annuum is the most widely cultivated and economically important species today. It produces both sweet, edible bell peppers and the majority of other common peppers. Paprika is obtained from the dried, powdered peppers of *Capsicum annuum*.

Other pungent kinds of peppers are obtained from *Capsicum fructescens*, including the pepper from which we obtain Tabasco sauce. Since their introduction to Europe, Asia and Africa, capsicum peppers have become integral parts of the cooking of these continents, and have partially replaced other hot spices.

Peppers are rated by heat, using a system called the Scoville scale, from 1 to 10. Mild peppers, such as peri peri, rate 1 or 2, and can be munched like apples. Habanero and scotch bonnet chilli peppers are among the hottest, and both rate 10. Their juice can cause blistering of exposed skin. In general, the smaller the chilli, the hotter it is, because it has proportionately more seeds.

Anyone who has eaten a hot chilli pepper can empathise with the searing pain, watering eyes and blinding sensation that occurs moments after the pepper hits the mouth. The burning sensation is caused by capsaicin, a compound concentrated in the fruit placenta, on which the seeds are borne. However, capsaicin has been studied recently for its medicinal qualities. Taken internally, it relaxes arteries and reduces blood pressure. In recent years, several drugs containing capsaicin have been produced, including creams that are applied locally to block the pain generated by arthritis, shingles, diabetes, neuralgia, and surgery. Native Mexicans have traditionally used chillies to treat toothache, among other ailments.

Capsicum peppers are most frequently grown as crop plants, but the diversity of fruit colour lends considerable ornamental value, and dwarf varieties in particular are well suited to cultivation in pots, window boxes and sunny conservatories.

The Eden Project has many varieties of capsicum peppers, which are displayed in the Tomatoes, Peppers and Aubergines exhibit.

26

chilli
pepper

It takes 454 kg. (1,000 lb.) of hot peppers to yield 137 mg. (1 oz.) of capsaicin – which is so potent that one drop diluted in 100,000 drops of water still produces a burning sensation!

1. *Capsicum annuum.*

2. Chilli peppers drying in the sun, New Mexico, USA. Drying preserves the chillis without destroying the hotness.

3. Ripe chillis displayed in gourds at a market in northern Nigeria.

4. Flame-roasting peppers in Arizona, USA.

As long ago as the 4th century BC, the Romans used cork to insulate their houses and beehives; as soles for sandals; stoppers for bottles, jugs and vases; floats for nets, and as buoys to aid navigation of their ships.

Popping the cork of a celebratory bottle of champagne, how many of us pause to think where that cork comes from?

Cork is obtained from the bark of the cork oak – *Quercus suber* – an evergreen tree that grows in open, park-like forests in Mediterranean regions, in areas with sandy, acidic soils, and temperatures rarely falling below -5°C (23°F). The tree has small, toothed, dark green leaves, and grows to a height of 15 m. (50 ft.). It has an average life expectancy of 170 to 200 years, and belongs to the beech family – Fagaceae.

Nearly all the commercially-exploited cork oak forests are in Portugal and Spain; Morocco, Algeria and Tunisia; southern France and Italy. Like gnarled old olives, cork oaks are a dominant feature of the Mediterranean landscape. Cork is obtained from the thick, deeply fissured, spongy outer bark of the tree that protects the inner bark against hot dry summer winds and damage from fire.

Cork comprises millions of minute, thick-walled cells, each with an air space in the centre. It is these air spaces that give cork its buoyancy in water. When compressed, cork forms an elastic substance. The combination of compressibility, and resistance to moisture and liquid penetration makes cork an extremely useful material.

The tree is first stripped of its harvest when it is 25 years old. This is an inferior bark that is mostly ground and processed as a composition cork. It is used for floor and wall tiles; in gaskets,

bottle caps, polishing wheels, and numerous other products. It is a good insulating material, and has even been used to insulate space ships. Successive crops are harvested every 9–12 years, and the products from these harvests are used in the manufacture of stoppers for wine bottles; barrel bungs; floats, and cork veneers. Cork is also an important source of tannins.

Cutting the natural raw material is a skilled job. If too much cork is removed at each harvest, the tree could die. A layer of cork is removed from the tree with a bevelled hatchet. Once the cork slabs have been stripped from the trees, they are stacked outdoors to flatten, and left for at least six months. The harvested cork is then steamed and sterilised. It becomes more flexible, and the slabs are scraped and trimmed, and then cut into standard, marketable sizes. Finally, the cork is graded and baled according to its thickness. It is quite common for a buyer to purchase the cork from an entire mountainside.

Cork is one of the world's most important renewable, non-timber forest products, and is an example of real sustainable land use. Many of the cork oak forests have been managed at a low intensity for centuries, resulting in forests of high biodiversity. Numerous important animal and plant species are becoming increasingly confined to these areas, as surrounding lands are used more intensively.

Other trees, besides *Q. suber,* have a thick layer of cork, and a number have been used around the world as substitutes for the oaks. Softwoods – willows and poplars –

have been used for bottle stoppers, as have the soft pith of elder and even sunflower. But no other bark combines all the favourable properties of cork oak bark, and none of the substitutes can compete with genuine cork as a large-scale commercial product.

cork oak

1. An avenue of cork oak – *Quercus suber* – in Portugal.

2. Stripping the bark from a cork oak, Portugal.

3. The bark is deeply fissured, and spongy.

A cork oak produces enough to cork 4,000 bottles per harvest!

4

5

Every day, enough cotton is harvested around the world to make 207 million T-shirts!

Cotton is the world's most important non-food crop, and in the USA it is bigger business than any other field crop.

Cotton belongs to the same family as hibiscus and the hollyhock – Malvaceae. There are some 39 species of cotton, which belong to the genus *Gossypium*. Most are tropical perennials, but in cultivation they are grown as annuals, generally in temperate climates. This ensures plants of short stature, uniformity of size and synchronous fruiting, which makes harvesting easier.

Cotton plants have beautiful, showy flowers, of cream, yellow or rose. After pollination, bolls develop, which contain the cotton fibres and resemble small balls of cotton wool. The fibres used to make cloth come from the outer surface of the seeds. Each fibre is a long seed-coat cell, and looks like a fine hair. Beneath the long fibres are shorter, fuzzy fibres, known as linters. In nature, these aid wind-dispersal of the seeds.

Only four species of *Gossypium* are cultivated on any scale commercially, but each has numerous subspecies, varieties and cultivars. *Gossypium hirsutum* – also called upland cotton – accounts for 95

per cent of commercial production. It is thought to have originated in north Brazil, and is known to have been grown for 5,000 years. It is favoured partly because of its greater resistance to boll weevil attack – a huge problem in America. Another popular species is *Gossypium barbadense* – a native of Northern Peru – whose long fibres produce a high quality, 'luxury' cotton.

By the 16th century, cotton had spread through the Americas, and to Africa and Eurasia. The British set up plantations in the Caribbean and southern USA, using slave labour to do the work. America produced more and more cotton for export to Britain, and the British cotton industry took off in the late 18th century, with the invention of new machinery to process cotton. In the 19th century, Liverpool was the centre of world trade in cotton. But various factors, including the American civil war, affected production. The British industry declined, and in the mid 20th century, most of the mills closed.

Today, cotton is huge business in China, the USA and India. In the early 1990s, China produced 3,830,000 tonnes a year; the USA

produced 3,690,000 tonnes. An American cotton farm can be as large as 1,000 ha. (2,500 a.), and the extensive use of machinery in harvesting and processing has enabled a dramatic increase in production. On modern farms, cotton plants are sprayed with defoliants when the boll is mature, to facilitate harvesting by machine. The bolls are then ginned – to separate the fibres from the seeds – and the fibres undergo extensive processing before being woven into cloth.

Cotton thread is also used in paper, nappies, wallpaper, bandages, and a myriad other everyday products. Oil is made from the seeds, which is used in soaps, margarine and cooking oils.

Today, there is much research into the production of organic cottons – particularly natural ways of getting rid of the boll weevil, because chemical spraying destroys soils and wildlife. The use of native plants is also being explored, because some have fibres of brown, cream, mauve or green, and aniline dyes can be very polluting.

The Eden Project's exhibit shows how cotton is grown, harvested and processed. It tells the history of cotton and focuses on new research world-wide.

1. Cotton flower, *Gossypium hirsutum*.
2. Cotton boll.
3. In the USA, most cotton is harvested by machine.
4. Machine-spinning cotton, Henan, China.
5. Indigo-dyed cotton cloth, Kano, Nigeria.

cotton

Cotton's short linter fibres are almost pure cellulose. They are used in gunpowder, dynamite, sausage skins, cellophane, nail polish and moulded plastic! The cellulose is also used to propel solid-fuel rockets; thicken ice-cream; make chewing gum chewy, and in makeup.

1. Grapes growing on a vine.
2. Wine is aged in casks, like these, or in bottles.

1

For a quality wine, the vine must be at least ten years old. The best wines come from vines over 30 years old.

Think of the Mediterranean, and you probably think of vineyards, and wine. As the Roman Empire expanded, vineyards were planted wherever the soil and climate were favourable – France, Spain, Portugal and Algeria. But winemaking is older than that – there is evidence of it in Iran as long ago as 3500 BC.

Today, grapes are cultivated commercially in warmer regions all over the world, particularly in western Europe; the Balkans; California;

Australia; South Africa, and parts of South America. There are some 8 million ha. (20 million a.) of vineyards world-wide – well over half of them in Europe. Between 60 and 70 million tonnes of grapes are produced each year – the two biggest producers being Italy and France.

The most widely cultivated species of grape is *Vitis vinifera* – the European wine grape. In 1860, European vines began to die from an infestation of Phylloxera, or root aphid. The insect came to

Europe on Californian rootstocks, and devastated thousands of hectares of vineyards in France alone. American species and hybrids showed high resistance to the insect, so Europe's vineyards were replanted with these Phylloxera-resistant rootstocks, on to which vines of *Vitis vinifera* were grafted. This practice is still carried out. Ironically, vines in California are currently suffering from Phylloxera outbreaks.

The grapevine is a woody perennial, belonging to the family Vitaceae. There are 65 species in the genus, but only a few are suitable for eating or winemaking. The vine climbs by means of tendrils. Palmately veined leaves arise alternately along the stem, and the greenish flowers are borne in clusters, from which the fruits develop after pollination.

grape

Grapevines in commercial vineyards are usually planted in spring, as year-old, rooted or grafted cuttings. They are generally planted around 3 m. (10 ft.) apart, and for the first couple of years all the shoots except the strongest one are pruned, so that the plants develop a strong main stem, resembling a small tree trunk. Most vines are trained on a trellis – the 'Guyet' system; but they may be grown without support – the 'Gobelet' system; or on pergolas, as is common in northern Portugal. After two years, the plants are allowed to bear fruit; then they are pruned again, to reduce the number of buds. This ensures that the shoots that develop are more prolific, and bear grapes of high quality.

Grapes have different uses, depending on their acidity and sugar content. Those used to make table wine have a relatively high acidity and moderate sugar content. Table grapes – of which there are at least 175 varieties – are low in both acidity and sugar, and make poor wine. Grapes used for dried fruit are preferably seedless, with high sugar content and low acidity. For juices and jellies, grapes grown in the eastern USA are preferred, because they have a strong flavour that enables them to withstand pasteurisation – a process used to prevent fermentation.

By far the biggest use of grapes is for winemaking. Wine is produced in temperate zones world-wide. It is made by a natural process of fermentation. The yeasts responsible for the fermentation of fruit sugars in the grape are usually present on the skin.

Grapes have many health benefits. They are said to have digestive and therapeutic properties; are rich in calories, and full of vitamins C and B. It is believed that red wine can help combat heart disease, and reports to that effect are thought to be responsible for the large increase in red wine sales in Britain in recent years.

The Eden Project's vineyard is growing grapes to make wine and dried fruit, as well as table grapes.

2

Millions of us start the day with a bowl of cornflakes - made from maize kernels. But long before Europeans knew about maize, it was a staple food of the Maya, Aztecs and Incas. Indeed, charred cobs found in southern Mexico have been dated to *c.* 3500 BC.

Maize - or corn as it is known in America - is a cereal grass, ranking with wheat and rice as one of the world's chief grain crops. The USA is the largest producer, with nearly 50 per cent of world production. Maize is the biggest crop in the USA, where it is grown for livestock feed (80 per cent); for export; and for making into a variety of food products. Most of the crop is grown in the Midwest region, known as the 'Corn Belt'. Other leading maize-growing nations are China, Russia, Brazil, and Mexico.

The maize plant - *Zea mays* - has an erect, solid stem, from 60 cm. (2 ft.) to 6 m. (20 ft.) in height, depending on the variety. The leaves grow alternately, and are long and narrow. The main stalk ends in a male inflorescence, or tassel, made up of many small flowers that produce pollen grains. The female inflorescence - the ear - is enclosed in modified leaves,

Maize has a high sugar content. It is processed to produce alcohol for use with gasoline, as gasohol. The dry stalk is a potentially important biofuel.

called husks. Silk fibres protrude from the tip of the ear, each attached to a female seed. Pollen from the tassels is carried by the wind and falls on to the silks, and pollinates the female seed. Each fertilised seed develops into a kernel.

Maize is native to the Americas, but its origin is a mystery. No wild plant even resembles it. By the 16th century, there were more than 300 local varieties; today there are thousands. Six general groups of varieties exist, differentiated by the characteristics of the kernel. They are dent, flint, pop, flour, sweet and pod. Dent is the most important commercial variety in the USA; followed by flint, which germinates at low temperatures, and is resistant to weevils. Pop - which

has small, hard kernels that pop when heated - is made into popcorn, and ground into cornmeal. It is grown extensively in the Andean regions of South America that were part of the Inca Empire. Sweet produces the vegetable sweetcorn: the sugar produced by the plant is not converted to starch during growth - hence the sweet flavour. Much of it is frozen or canned soon after harvest, to preserve its flavour. Pod is grown as a decorative plant.

The most important advance in maize cultivation was the introduction of hybrids in the 1930s. Of the thousands now available, one or more flourishes in almost any combination of soil and climate. Yield increases of 25 to 50 per cent have been attributed to hybrids.

3

4

Corn oil is a by-product of the maize-milling industry. It is used as a cooking and salad oil, and in solid form as margarine. It is also used in the manufacture of paints, soaps, and linoleum.

1. Maize growing in Mexico.
2. Yellow and blue corn drying in the sun in New Mexico, USA.
3. Head of sweetcorn.
4. Cooking corn *tortillas*, Yucatan, Mexico.

Today, maize is an important food staple in many countries. An excellent source of carbohydrates, it has the same number of calories as wheat or rice, but is low in protein. In Central and South America, maize is used to make sweet porridge; *tamales*, *tortillas* and *tacos* – all of which may be filled with beans, pepper and meat; and *chica* – a beer.

Cornflour and maize thicken a huge range of processed foods. Glucose syrups for sweetening drinks are made from maize starch, which is also used in the manufacture of cosmetics, pharmaceuticals, and adhesives. Maize is important in modern brewing operations, and is used to produce industrial alcohol.

maize

1

2

Olives are among the oldest commercially grown crops. They are native to the eastern Mediterranean region, and have been important for more than 5,000 years.

The olive is a member of the Oleaceae family – a small group of woody, flowering plants, which includes ash, lilac, privet, jasmine, and forsythia. The olive – *Olea* – contains about 20 species. They are evergreen shrubs or trees, which can grow to a height of about 20 m. (66 ft.). In cultivation, they are usually kept at 3 m. (10 ft.), making it easier to reach the fruits.

Young olives have smooth, slender and pliable stems, silver-grey in colour. They become fissured, rigid and contorted in advanced maturity, with a much darker colour. The leaves are silvery-green, and small white flowers are produced in summer. The fruits develop in clusters – green to purple, depending on ripeness – and contain a large, single stone.

The ancient Egyptians and Greeks used olive oil to anoint bodies; as a cleanser, lamp oil, medicine, and foodstuff; and in religious ceremonies. The leaves of the olive have antiseptic and calming properties, and were used to lower fevers and blood pressure.

Today, the olive tree – *Olea europaea* – is cultivated largely for its fruit. Other species are grown for foliage; and a few, including *Olea capensis* – black ironwood of southern Africa – for timber. The wood is hard and variegated, and valued in cabinet-making.

Olives are widely cultivated throughout Europe – growing in valley meadows and on hillside terraces – and in other parts of the world with a Mediterranean-type climate. An increased awareness of the health benefits of olive oil has led to a significant increase in consumption world-wide; and the olive oil business is now worth US$10 billion a year. Major producers include Spain, Italy, Turkey, Greece, Tunisia, Morocco and California. Some 10 million ha. (25 million a.) of olive groves around the world produce about 13 million tonnes of olives each year. The Mediterranean region produces 95 per cent of the crop, and 80 per cent of the products are consumed there. Only 1 or 2 per cent of the world's olive crop is eaten as fruit – most is pressed for oil.

Olives are quite acidic. They contain a compound called oleuropein, which must be broken down to make them palatable. Ripe olives are treated with sodium

The olive is deep-rooted; slow to mature, and very long-lived. Some trees are several hundred years old.

hydroxide, to hydrolyse the bitter oleuropein. Treated olives turn black when exposed to air; green olives are kept submerged after processing, to retain their colour.

Olive oil is one of the few oils obtained from a fruit pulp, rather than from seeds. The fruit picked for oil must be quite ripe, and in Mediterranean countries the ripe olives are harvested by hand, in late autumn and winter. The ripe fruits contain about 20 per cent oil. They are macerated; the seeds removed, and the pulp pressed.

The first press – a cold press – yields virgin olive oil, which has a low acidity and the best flavour. Subsequent pressings – usually with heat – yield oils of lower grades. Olive oil is used mostly in cooking, but also in canning, and as a table oil.

An inferior oil – pomace – is produced by grinding olive stones, and is used to make soap. The residues from oil production can be used as animal feed, and other uses of the by-products of the olive industry are being researched.

olive

It has been suggested that the ancient Egyptians, when building pyramids, slid the enormous blocks of stone over one another by placing olives, or olive oil, between them.

1. Ripe olives, *Olea europaea*, on a tree.
2. Olive trees are precious and can live to a grand old age. Sometimes they need propping up!
3. Old olive press in Andalusia, southern Spain.
4. Olive trees growing in southern Spain.
5. Olive groves in an arid landscape in southern Spain.

Citrus fruits are a part of many breakfasts – whether as fruit juices, grapefruit halves or marmalade. The production and processing of citrus fruits is a huge global industry, and it is hard to imagine that only 100 years ago the orange was an expensive luxury, prescribed as a remedy for colds and consumption.

Orange is the common name for the citrus fruit, of the family Rutaceae. There are a wide variety of oranges, including the sweet orange – *Citrus sinensis* – the sour, or Seville, orange – *Citrus aurantium* – and the mandarin orange, or tangerine – *Citrus reticulata*. The fruit is technically a hesperidium – a kind of berry. It consists of several easily separated carpels, or sections – each with several seeds and many juice cells – covered by a leathery skin containing numerous oil glands. Orange trees are usually evergreen, seldom exceeding 9 m. (30 ft.) in height, with oval, glossy leaves and white, fragrant flowers. The leaves, flowers, and rind of the fruit abound in volatile oils and emit a sharp fragrance – a characteristic of the citrus family.

Citrus are native to South-East Asia. It is thought that the orange resulted from a cross between a tangerine and a pomelo. Oranges were introduced to Spain by the Moors in about the 12th century. In the 16th century, the Spanish and Portuguese took them to the Americas. Rich in vitamin C, they were found to prevent scurvy on long sea voyages, and became an essential food item on board ship. This promoted their spread around the world.

Today, with an annual harvest of some 62.5 million tonnes, the sweet orange is the most widely grown fruit in the world – surpassed only by apples and bananas in quantity produced and consumed.

Important producing areas are the USA, the Caribbean, Israel, and South and Central America. Until recently, the USA was the world's largest producer of citrus fruits, but it has been superseded by Brazil. These countries produce over 40 per cent of the world citrus crop, but most of their production is processed, not eaten fresh.

In the USA, Florida is the leading producer of oranges: they rank as the state's most valuable crop. Here, and in other orange-growing states, Valencia is the most common variety of sweet orange. Another important variety is the Washington navel orange, imported from Bahia, Brazil, in 1870. The navel is a seedless orange, within which a second small (or abortive) orange grows. The sour orange is cultivated to a limited extent for marmalade, and to provide rootstock for less vigorous strains.

About 20 per cent of the global orange crop is sold as whole fruit; the remainder is used in preparing frozen and canned orange juice, extracts, and preserves. Pectin – the setting agent in many preserves and jams – is extracted from the peel; citric acid – widely used in flavourings – from the fruit. Three essential oils are obtained from oranges: oil of orange – used principally as a flavouring agent – comes from the rind of the fruit; oil of petigrain – used in perfumery – comes from the leaves and twigs; and oil of neroli – used in flavourings and perfumes – comes from the blossoms.

As you walk among the Eden Project's citrus groves, find out more about the history, cultivation and uses of the fruits. Then sample the fruits in the restaurant, and taste the foods that have been made from them!

The flavour of Earl Grey tea comes from the oil of the bergamot orange, extracted from the rind of the fruit.

1. Oranges growing on a tree, Jamaica.
2. Oranges treated with ethylene are really orange.
3. A roadside stall in Jamaica, selling oranges and other fruit.

Fully ripe oranges are not always orange! The formation of the orange pigment, carotene, is promoted by cool temperatures, so in warm temperatures, oranges often remain mottled yellow and green. Commercial growers routinely spray oranges with the ripening hormone ethylene, to ensure orange-coloured fruit.

orange

39

The prickly pear belongs to the genus *Opuntia* – one of the largest groups of plants in the cactus family. The name *Opuntia* comes from a spiny plant associated with the ancient Greek town of Opus.

Only a dozen species of *Opuntia* are known as prickly pear, and all are characterised by flat, fleshy pads, called 'phyllodes', which are green or greyish-green in colour, and covered with spines. The spines are modified leaves, or 'glochids', which protect the plant from predation. The prickly pear flowers from April to June, with yellow, orange or reddish flowers that develop into warty, pear-shaped, edible fruits. In the wild, these are a food source for rodents and birds.

The prickly pear is native to Mexico. One of the most common species is the *Opuntia ficus-indica* – more commonly known as the Indian fig. Its original habitat is not known, but it is widely naturalised in the Mediterranean region, where it grows in dry, rocky places, often alongside another introduced plant, the agave. *Opuntia ficus-indica* is an evergreen perennial that grows to 5 m. (16 ft.) by 5 m. It has yellow flowers, and fruit that grow to 10 cm. (4 in.) long, varying in colour from yellow to purple, depending on the variety. This species is not as spiny as other prickly pears.

The Indian fig has many uses. The edible fruit can be eaten raw or cooked, or can be dried for later use. It is a sweet fruit, and very refreshing, with the flavour of a watermelon. It is sold in greengrocers and supermarkets in Mediterranean countries, and is starting to be seen in British supermarkets. The pads of the plant can be cooked and eaten as a vegetable; the flowers can be eaten raw, and the seed can be ground into a meal. An edible gum is obtained from the stem.

The plant also has medicinal uses. The flowers are astringent, and are used to reduce bleeding and treat problems of the gastro-intestinal tract. The flowers and stems have antispasmodic, diuretic and emollient qualities.

There are over 200 species of *Opuntia*, ranging in size – height and width – from several metres to a few centimetres.

The gum obtained from the stem can be mixed with oil to make candles, and the sticky juice of the boiled stem segments can be added to building plaster for better adhesion. The Indian fig is also used to make red dye and face-creams, and to purify water. A truly versatile plant!

The prickly pear is cultivated in warm temperate and sub-tropical regions for its edible fruits, and as a stock-proof barrier. It also makes an attractive houseplant or conservatory plant. It needs full sun and low humidity, and prefers sandy soils that should be kept fairly dry. It is best propagated by cuttings of leaf pads, which root very readily. But beware! The glochids on the leaf pads are easily detached from the plant, and difficult to remove from the skin.

The plant can also be grown easily from seed. Indeed, many of the Eden Project's *Opuntia* were donated by people who grew them from seed, taken from fruit eaten on holiday. You can see *Opuntia ficus-indica* in the wild Mediterranean area.

prickly pear

The prickly pear was introduced to Australia and South Africa in the 19th century, and soon became an invasive weed, causing problems to farmers. Its spread is now thought to be under control – due the importation of its natural predator, a moth!

1. Prickly pear growing wild in Mexico.
2. Yellow flower of *Opuntia ficus-indica*.
3. Flower and swelling fruits of *Opuntia ficus-indica*.
4. Fruits of wild prickly pear, Spain.

Cornwall is famous for its golden saffron cakes. According to local legend, the Phoenicians came to Cornwall for tin, for which they bartered saffron. The introduction of saffron to Britain has also been attributed to a 14th-century pilgrim, who risked his life to bring a single saffron corm to his native town of Chypping Walden, in Essex.

Saffron – *Crocus sativus* – is a hardy, autumn-flowering crocus of the iris family, Iridaceae. Saffron has voluptuous, purple-blue petals; chive-green leaves; fluffy, yellow stamens, and rage-red stigmas, which are picked, dried, and sold as the spice saffron. It is estimated that 462,000 stigma branches from 154,000 flowers are required to produce a kilogram of saffron – which is why saffron is the most expensive spice in the world. In times of scarcity, its price has exceeded that of gold.

Saffron originates from either the Far East or southern Europe. In Tudor times, it was produced in Britain on a grand scale. It brought great wealth to Chypping Walden, and in 1514, Henry VIII changed the town's name to Saffron Walden. Today, saffron is imported to Britain. Spain is the leading producer, supplying around 70 per cent of the global market, mostly from La Mancha. Saffron is also cultivated in southern Europe; Morocco and the Middle East; China; Kashmir, and India.

Saffron was first recognised as a versatile, water-soluble, heat-stable dye. It has given warm, golden tones to Roman togas, Tudor ruffs, Indian saris, and even the wraps of Egyptian mummies. The Persians favoured it as a dye for sheep- and goatskins, and used it in their carpet industry.

Saffron was the only spice ever cultivated in, and exported from, England.

The natural dye found in saffron is crocin, which also provides an aromatic, and a flavouring agent that delights the taste-buds. Saffron is used by the cosmetic and perfume industries, and in the distillation of liqueurs. It has medicinal qualities, and has been used as a folk remedy for scarlet fever, smallpox, colds, insomnia, asthma, tumours and cancer. It was even believed to be an effective antidote to the plague.

Saffron is one of the world's richest sources of riboflavin and vitamin B_2, but its main use today is to colour and flavour food – paella in Spain; risotto in Italy; rice dishes in the Middle East; bouillabaisse in France; sculptured saffron buns at Christmas in Sweden, and, of course, saffron cake in Cornwall.

Because of the high price of saffron, a number of substitutes are produced. Turmeric, safflower, annatto seeds, marigold petals and corn stigmas have all been used. But none of them has the intense colour, nor the distinctive flavour and aroma of saffron. So, despite its price, chefs prefer saffron.

You can grow saffron in a loamy, well-drained, nutrient-rich soil. Plant corms in June or July, at depths of 12–14 cm. (5–6 in.), and expect a harvest from mid October. (It will take a few years for the crocus to flower properly.) Pick the flowers the morning they show – with the flower heads closed – then remove the long, red stigmas by hand, and dry them immediately.

5 4

saffron

Experienced removers of saffron stigmas in Spain are called *mondadoras*. They can remove the stigmas from 10,000 flowers per day!

1. *Crocus sativus*.
2. Picking the flowers of *Crocus sativus* in La Mancha, Spain.
3. Grandmother and granddaughter removing the stigmas from crocus flowers, La Mancha, Spain.
4. Cornish saffron cake.
5. Dried saffron.

The Eden Project's agave –
Agave americana – is one
of the biggest in Britain.
It is nearly 3 m. (10 ft.)
tall by 3 m. wide.

A plant from which we produce a smooth clear spirit, and rope strong enough to moor ships? That must be the agave!

Agaves are unusual plants – not just because of their succulent character and amazing, sword-like leaves, but because of the special role they have played in the indigenous civilisations of Central America. They have supplied people with food, drink, fibre and shelter for thousands of years, and are still plants of great economic importance.

Various parts of the plant are edible, and have been an important source of food for humans and cattle, particularly in desert regions. The cuticle of the leaf has also been used as a wrapper for *tortillas* and other foods – an archaic forerunner of modern cling film! Fibres from the tough leaves of *Agave pacifica* were used by the Aztecs, instead of cotton, to make clothes. The roots of some species yield a pulp that produces a lather when wet and is used as a soap.

The sub-tropical agave originated in Central America, but certain species are widely naturalised in Mediterranean countries, and are used increasingly as architectural plants in landscape design around Britain. The Agave family contains over 300 species. Many are small and composed of rosettes of short, fleshy leaves coated with wax, which are armed with formidable spines along their margins. The best known is the *Agave americana*, commonly known as the American aloe, or Century plant. The latter

name came from the belief that this agave flowers once every 100 years. In fact, it flowers every 30 years! Many agaves have huge flower spikes, and that of *Agave americana* can reach 12 m. (40 ft.) in height.

The most famous use of agave must be in the production of tequila – responsible for many hangovers around the world! Tequila is distilled liquor. The distilling process was developed in Mexico after European colonisation. Today, it is of significant economic importance to Mexico, and the industry is expanding rapidly.

Tequila comes from the leaf-base of the agave, from the species *Agave tequilana* (which is almost impossible to obtain outside Mexico). The plant is cooked in ovens, and its raw starches are converted to sugars. They are macerated and allowed to ferment in large

vats, until the sugars are changed bacterially to alcohol. This manufacturing process has been carried out for 150 years in the state of Jalisco, in and around the town of Tequila, from which the product takes its official name.

Until the mid 20th century, rope and cord were made from plant fibres, especially from sisal, which is prepared from the leaves of the agave. The two main species used for sisal are *Agave sisalana* and *Agave fourcroydes*. The leaf fibres are often about 1 m. (3 ft.) long, and are very strong. In recent years, sisal production has diminished due to the use of synthetic fibres; but sisal is naturally hard-wearing and resistant to sunlight, and these qualities have ensured its continuing use. *Agave sisalana* is still grown in large plantations in Brazil and East Africa, and until recently was grown in Spain.

agave

1. Century plant – *Agave americana* – at the Eden Project's nursery.
2. The Century plant flowers like this every ... 30 years!
3. A field of sisal – *Agave sisalana* – in Yucatan, Mexico.
4. Sisal rope for sale in a market in Mexico.
5. Tequila sunrise! The Mexican drink tequila is made from the leaves of *Agave tequilana*.

2 3

1

Koala bears eat from 0.5 to 1 kg. (1–2 lb.) of eucalyptus leaves each night, and the bees of Australia feed on the nectar. Eucalypts produce some of the finest honeys, and each species has its own characteristic flavour and colour.

Eucalypts – *Eucalyptus* – are some of the most characteristic species of Australia; but they have adapted to different environments, and have been introduced widely around the world. They now dominate huge areas outside Australia – even causing a nuisance in some regions, by their very invasive nature.

Economically, eucalypts are the most important group of plants in the myrtle family – Myrtaceae – which contains over 600 species. They are fast-growing, evergreen perennials,

varying in habit from dwarf shrubs to some of the tallest trees in the world. They have a variety of bark forms and textures that are of great ornamental value, and which aid botanists in identification.

Some eucalypts have evolved to survive fire. *Mallees* grow as dense shrubs or small trees, with multiple trunks emerging from large, hori-

Eucalyptus have both juvenile and adult leaves, which differ in shape, position and colour. The juvenile leaves are thought to act as a protection mechanism against predators and climate.

zontal, underground lignotubers – modified root systems – which resprout after the tree has been burnt to the ground.

In the wild, harvester ants eat the seeds of many species of eucalypts. However, after a fire, more seeds are dropped than can be consumed by the ants, so they store the excess in underground nests.

Some of these uneaten seeds germinate, resulting in the natural regeneration of the habitat after fire.

Eucalyptus trees are grown world-wide for timber. Their heavy, hard and durable wood; exceptionally fast growth; rapid regenerative properties after being cut back hard; and their great size make them ideal as a timber plantation tree.

Eucalypt timber is used in construction and boat-building; in the manufacture of furniture, plywood, veneers, and wood-chip; as railway sleepers, and as parts of musical instruments. It is also used in the production of paper and fibreboard. However, the use of eucalyptus for timber has been of great concern to conservationists for many years – first, because of the destruction by loggers of the trees and habitats in their natural environment, with the clearance of land of native plants; and second, because of the introduction of eucalyptus into other countries as monoculture plantations.

Eucalypts have other economic uses, apart from timber. Volatile or essential oils, occurring in the leaves, bark, buds, flowers and young fruits are rich in cineole – an active ingredient in inhalants, gargles, sprays and lozenges that soothe the throat and provide antiseptic qualities. The oils are also a source of rutin, used in vitamins that assist in the use and adsorption of vitamin C; and of piperitene, from which thymol and menthol are manufactured, for disinfectants and deodorants. Eucalyptus oils are also used in perfumes – particularly *E. citriodora*, which gives a lemon scent.

In some countries, eucalypts are of great ornamental and horticultural value, as shade or street trees, windbreaks and shelter-belts. Their evergreen, fragrant, glaucous blue foliage is ideal for use in floristry. Their fast-growing nature makes them an important fuel crop in some regions, and they are used widely by eco-engineers to control soil erosion. A further use is for tannin extracts, used in leather production.

Cornwall's mild, maritime climate lets us grow some of the more tender species of eucalyptus out of doors. See different species in the Temperate, Warm Temperate and Humid Tropics biomes.

eucalyptus

1. Eucalyptus leaves.
2. Eucalypts are ideal trees for timber plantations.

Eucalyptus regnans is the tallest hardwood tree in the world. Some trees felled in the 19th century measured 140 m. (460 ft.)!

2 1

What makes a good pint? Barley malt, hops, yeast and water for starters. Hops define beer as a specific type of alcoholic beverage, and are vital in determining beer styles. Their control in the brewing process is essential for brand identity.

The hop - *Humulus lupulus* - is a tall, climbing, herbaceous perennial, native to Europe and the Middle East. It is one of a small number of species closely related to the cannabis plant. Hops exist as separate male and female plants. Male plants are used in breeding. Female plants produce cones, or lupulin, that contain resins - the chemicals vital for brewing. The most important of these are the alpha acids, which confer bitterness. Their preservative properties are important in beer production.

The earliest known use of hops was 4,000 years ago, as a means of preserving yeast for brewing and baking. Ancient Egyptians used them to make a fermented drink, called *symthum*.

Hops came into general use in England at the end of the 15th century. Traditionally, they were grown in hop hills: a mound of compost was built around the base of the plant, and the stem was wrapped around a chestnut post. This led to the 19th-century system involving structures of wire, poles and string, erected by men on stilts. Today, the stilt-men are rarely seen - they have been replaced by tractors and hydraulic systems.

Apart from brewing, hops have a variety of uses. They were a medicinal herb in ancient Egypt, and later in Europe they treated liver disease and digestive complaints. The Romans ate hop shoots as we eat asparagus. In Sweden, hop fibres made coarse cloth and paper. Today, hops are more prized for their soft, sensuous aromas, which are important in essential oils and essences.

The main varieties grown in the UK today are: Wye Target,

3

Beer manufacture utilises 98 per cent of the world's production of hops.

Goldings, Northdown, Bramling Cross, Challenger, Fuggle and Northdown. These are harvested in September. Bines - hop plants laden with cones - are cut to 1 m. (3 ft.) above the ground, and carted off-field, where the cones are separated from the leaves and stem. The cones are dried in kilns, or oast houses, and packed into pockets - bales - for despatch to breweries, or for further processing.

Although there are many varieties of hops, there are only three basic types - aroma hops, which are used generally as a finishing or conditioning hop in brewing; bitter hops, from which bitterness is extracted during boiling; and dual-purpose hops, which are used in both processes.

Hops are used in the brewing process in a number of forms. Whole hops - the natural hop cones that have been dried and baled - are the traditional way to

brew. Hop pellets - made from ground and compressed whole hops, held together by natural resins - need less storage space and have a better consistency. But the grinding process changes the behaviour of the hop, and the flavour of the beer.

Many breweries around the world use a liquefied hop extract, which retains the all-important resins, and discards the vegetable matter. Advantages are consistency; minimal deterioration; greater utilisation, and the need for less storage space. But again, the hop's character is changed in the extraction process.

The Eden Project's Beer and Brewing exhibit includes plants related to brewing, such as malting barley and hops. Displays show traditional and modern ways of hop-growing - from tall plants on individual stakes, to the dwarf hop hedges being developed today.

hop

1. Hop plant – *Humulus lupulus* – female, with cones.
2. Men on stilts training the bines on a hop farm in Kent, in the mid 20th century.
3. Adding hops to the copper during the brewing process.

49

The Romans steeped the leaves and stems of lavender in their bathing water, and this practice gave the species its Latin name – *Lavandula* – which comes from the verb *lavare* – 'to bathe'. The Romans were responsible for the spread of lavender throughout Europe.

Lavandula belongs to the mint family – Lamiaceae – and is distributed in dry, stony or rocky places throughout the Mediterranean, North Africa, the Canary Islands, India and the Middle East. Lavender is relished as a perfume, a culinary herb and a medicinal cure. Other plants in the family – basils, mints, rosemaries, sages and thymes – are well-known culinary herbs.

There are over 20 species of lavender. They are evergreen, shrubby plants, with silvery green leaves, blue-purple flowers, and woody stems. All parts of the plants, except the roots, contain essential oils which, in the wild, provide the plants with defence mechanisms against the hot dry summers in which they grow. They are thought to prevent water loss; their bitter taste renders them inedible to most pests and livestock; and their fragrant smells attract pollinating insects. The volatile oils of some species may combust spontaneously in high temperatures, and play a role in natural fire cycles. Certain Mediterranean species germinate only after a fire, so some horticulturists use a commercially produced 'smoke water' to germinate them in cultivation.

Lavender is used mostly in the perfume industry. Synthetic perfumes tend to lack the fine aroma of its essential oils, so lavender is still in demand. It is grown commercially by Alpine farmers in the mountains of Provence in the south of France, and is also produced in Britain, Spain, Australia and the USA. In Britain, the first and biggest centre for lavender growing was Mitcham in Surrey. It was also cultivated and distilled in Hertfordshire, Lincolnshire and Norfolk. Today, it is grown commercially in Norfolk.

Lavandula angustifolia – known as true lavender, or English lavender – produces the highest quality oil, and grows at altitudes of 800–1,300 m. (2,600–4,300 ft.). Another species grown for its oils is *Lavandula latifolia*, which grows at between 600 and 800 m. (2,000–2,600 ft.). It yields up to three times more essential oil than *L. angustifolia*, but the oil is inferior. Today, a hybrid of these two species is the main type in cultivation. This hybrid – *Lavandula* x *intermedia* 'Grosso' – produces a poorer quality oil, called lavandin. But it can be grown at much lower altitudes, and yields at least four or five times as much essential oils as true lavender. In many lavender products, higher quality oils are mixed with hybrid oils.

Commercial growers plant lavender in autumn or spring. Flowers appear in June, and are harvested when they are in full bloom – when the essential oils are at their peak. Lavender used to be cut by hand, with scythes, but today all the large farms are mechanised. The cut flowers are left to dry, and then they are bundled and packed for the distillery.

Lavender has long been a popular plant in European cottage gardens. The dried flowers are used to make pot-pourri and sachets to scent rooms, cupboards and linens, and to repel moths. For hundreds of years, lavender was a staple herb in many kitchens, and its culinary popularity is slowly returning. Its leaves and flowers can be made into tea, and used in salads, vinegars, jellies, ice-creams and soft drinks. Bees that visit lavender flowers produce a distinctive, rich flavoured honey.

lavender

Our swathe of lavender recreates the ambience of Provence. In summer, you will be charmed by purple flowers, and delicious fragrances.

Lavender can be used as an antiseptic to help heal wounds and burns. The essential oils can be burned to relieve stress and headaches, and for this reason, lavender is still used in many hospitals.

1. *Lavandula angustifolia.*
2. Harvesting lavender. All the large farms are mechanised.
3. Lavender field in Provence, France.

From Liquorice Allsorts to Pontefract Cakes, liquorice is a sweet we love or loathe. But liquorice is a most versatile plant, with many more uses than confectionery.

Liquorice belongs to the genus *Glycyrrhiza*, and is part of the legume family. The word *Glycyrrhiza* comes from the Greek words *glykys* (sweet), and *rhiza* (root). There are about 20 species in this genus, only a few of which are used. The perennial herb *Glycyrrhiza glabra* is the species commonly known as liquorice. It grows to 1.2 m. (4 ft.) by 1 m. (3 ft.), and flowers between June and July, with pale blue to violet flowers.

It is native to temperate regions of the Northern hemisphere, where it grows on dry scrubland and in damp ditches. The useful part is the root, which is harvested when the plant is three or four years old, and the fibrous roots have developed. Cultivars of liquorice include 'Pontefract', 'Poznan' and 'Russian'. Of these, 'Poznan' is the sweetest and most commonly grown.

Liquorice is known to have been used medicinally 6,000 years ago, by the Assyrians. Greek and Roman soldiers carried its roots to quench their thirst on long marches. The first reported cultivation of liquorice in England was in 1562, by monks in Pontefract, Yorkshire, and liquorice became important in the manufacture of Pontefract Cakes. In the early 20th century, Charlie Thompson, a traveller for a local firm, stumbled out of a hostelry and accidentally dropped his box of samples. Undeterred, he pushed them all together, and sold a new line in sweets – Liquorice Allsorts!

By the 19th century, the British demand for liquorice had outstripped local supplies, and it started to be sourced elsewhere. Labour costs were less abroad, and foreign liquorice began to replace the locally grown. Land pressures around Pontefract, and the need to produce food crops, also led to a reduction in the crop. Chocolate became more fashionable than liquorice, and the last Pontefract crop was lifted in 1965 – for pharmaceutical use.

Liquorice has long been used both as a medicine and as a flavouring to disguise the unpleasant taste of other medications, and it is still one of the most common herbs in Western herbal medicine. It is very sweet, moist, and soothing. It detoxifies and protects the liver, and is a powerful anti-inflammatory, which is used in conditions as varied as arthritis and mouth ulcers. It is also used to treat conditions such as catarrh, asthma, eczema and shingles. However, a gross overdose can cause oedema, high blood pressure, and congestive heart failure!

Liquorice has many edible uses. Liquorice powder extracted from the root is used in sweets, baked goods, ice-cream, soft drinks, stout and beer. It gives stout its characteristic thickness and blackness. The sweet flavour of liquorice is derived from the root, which contains glycyrrhizin – one of the sweetest natural compounds known, which is 50 times sweeter than sugar. The dried root is used for chewing and for teething children, and as a tooth cleaner. A tea made from the roots is an excellent thirst quencher.

The Eden Project's Liquorice exhibit contains different cultivars. The crops will be harvested to explain how liquorice is produced. The liquorice-derived products on display show its versatility as a crop.

4

3

5

1. *Glycyrrhiza glabra*, commonly known as liquorice, is a perennial herb.
2. Stamping out Pontefract Cakes by hand, at a factory in Yorkshire, mid 20th century.
3. Liquorice root, which is 50 times sweeter than sugar!
4. Pontefract Cakes.
5. Liquorice Allsorts.

liquorice

90 per cent of the world crop of liquorice is used in American cigarettes.

It flavours the tobacco, keeps it moist, and ensures even burning.

Extracts from liquorice roots are used as a foaming agent in beers and fire extinguishers! The waste fibres are used in insulation and fibreboard.

The monkey-puzzle tree is a remarkable and rare conifer in our own backyards. Conifers, or gymnosperms, live on all the continents of the world except Antarctica, and tolerate a wide range of climatic and ecological conditions. There are from 630 to 800 different species, of which 25 per cent are threatened with extinction. One of these is *Araucaria araucana*, better known as the monkey-puzzle tree.

The monkey-puzzle is thought to have been introduced into the UK by Archibald Menzies, who accompanied Captain Vancouver on a round-the-world voyage in the late 18th century. It is said that on his travels he pocketed some nuts served at a Chilean banquet, and took them home. In the wild, the monkey-puzzle tree is found only in the northern extremes of South American temperate sub-Antarctic forest, its main natural habitat being the high Andean range of Chile and Argentina.

In southern Chile, the monkey-puzzle is highly prized, and regarded with symbolic and spiritual importance by the Araucano people. Its seeds, or *piñones*, have long been a staple food. They are rich in starch, soft like cashew nuts, and taste a little like pine nuts. They are delicious raw, toasted or boiled, and are often ground into flour, and used as a condiment in soups, or to make bread. *Piñones* are also used to make a fermented beverage called *chavid*.

The monkey-puzzle is under threat and is listed as vulnerable in the *Global Red List of Conifers*.

During the late summer the Araucanos collect the seeds from the ground for personal consumption, to feed to their livestock, and to sell to merchants in lowland towns. To ensure a good harvest of *piñones*, the Araucanos make offerings during an annual ritual called *Ngillatun*. *Piñones* are used occasionally in burials, and a sacred monkey-puzzle tree in the northern part of its range is the object of an annual pilgrimage for many Araucanos.

The timber industry has long valued the monkey-puzzle as its wood – sold as Chilean Pine – contains few big knots, and a large quantity of timber can be obtained from one tree. One of its first industrial uses was for railroad ties.

Later, it was used to make tunnels, carriages, pillars, drawing tables, ladders, skis, piano interiors, oars and rulers. It was even used in aeroplane construction. More conventional uses of the wood include beams, doors, floors, window frames, stairs, plywood, crating and furniture. Today, felling monkey-puzzles is strictly prohibited, except in special circumstances, and national nature reserves have been set up to protect them.

The Eden Project is working alongside Martin Gardner, Coordinator of the International Conifer Conservation Programme of the Royal Botanic Gardens, Edinburgh, in collaboration with the University of Edinburgh and the Universidad Austral de Chile, Valdivia. With permission from the Chilean authorities, Martin Gardner and his colleagues collected seed from individual trees in the wild, to represent natural populations. These were brought to the UK, with associated scientific documentation, and germinated. Our outdoor Chilean temperate rainforest will be one of several places in the UK growing a genetic replica forest of monkey-puzzle trees to help safeguard their survival for the future.

3

monkey-puzzle

1. *Araucaria araucana*, showing the cone.
2. The bark of the monkey-puzzle is deeply fissured.
3. *Araucaria araucana* growing wild on a mountainside in Chile.

1

2

The monkey-puzzle tree grows to nearly 50 m. (164 ft.) high, with basal diameters of 2.5 m. (8 ft.). In the wild, it commonly lives to be 1,300 years old!

In Peru, the sunflower was worshipped by the Aztecs as an emblem of the Sun God. In France, it inspired the paintings of Vincent Van Gogh. Today, although it is grown for its ornamental value, nearly 90 per cent of world production of sunflowers is for the manufacture of vegetable oil.

The sunflower - *Helianthus annuus* - originated in the south-west of North America, and occurs naturally in scrubland and disturbed habitats. It belongs to one of the largest flowering plant families in the world - the daisy family - which comprises well over 20,000 species. There are over 50 species of *Helianthus*, and hundreds of varieties of *H. annuus*.

Each flower head is composed of two types of tiny flower, with up to 1,000 flowers per head - hence the scientific family name, *Compositae*. The two types of flowers are ray florets - the outer yellow parts, and disc florets - the central black parts. The latter develop into the seeds, from which we obtain oil.

However, the sunflower boasts many other uses. Traditionally, Native North Americans ate the seeds raw and used them to make flour or meal. The Hopi people used particular types of sunflower seeds to make brilliant blue, purple, black or red dyes for their woven textiles, pottery,

and body paints. They used the stems and leaves in basket and textile production, and various other parts in medicines. The Dakota made a broth of sunflower heads to relieve chest pains, and the Pueblo used part of the plant to treat rattlesnake and spider bites, and to heal cuts and wounds.

In other parts of the world, the sunflower has had many different uses. The stems have been used to make fibre and paper. The central parts of the stems - the pith - have a specific gravity less than cork, and have been used in lifebelts and other buoyancy products. In the Caucasus, the sunflower was used as a substitute for quinine in the treatment of malaria.

Today, the leaves and seeds of the sunflower are used in health food products, animal feeds, birdseed for garden and pet birds, and pet foods. The seeds are also used in confectionery. The sunflower is of great ornamental value, and Japanese varieties, bred

to release less pollen, are favoured in the cut-flower industry.

It was not until 1779, in Bavaria, that sunflower seeds were first used as a commercial source of oil. Today, sunflowers are grown commercially in all countries with temperate climates, and the sunflower is one of the most important crops for vegetable oil production. It is Russia's most important oil crop. From the 1930s to the 1950s, the Russians bred sunflowers to increase the oil content of the seed to 50 per cent, and produced flower heads that exceeded 30 cm. (1 ft.) in diameter, for better yields.

Sunflower oil is thought to be healthier than many other oils, because of its low-saturated, fatty acid content. Saturated fatty acids are associated with excessive cholesterol build-up in blood vessels, and therefore with heart disease.

The Eden Project's exhibit covers world production of the sunflower, and explains how the oil is extracted.

Sunflower oil is used mainly in cooking oils, margarines and salad dressings. Special varieties have been developed for industrial oils, paints and lubricants.

3

2

56

1. *Helianthus annuus* is grown commercially in countries with temperate climates.
2. *Helianthus annuus* 'Sonja'.
3. Fields of sunflowers in Spain.

1

sunflower

Sunflowers are unusually heliotropic. The flowers track the sun's path across the sky.

grance of the sweet pea are as popular now as in Victorian times. Yet few people know how the plant was bred to become the splendid frilled flower it is today.

Sweet peas – *Lathyrus odoratus* – are among 150 species of the genus *Lathyrus*, a member of the pea family. The word *Lathyrus* comes from the Greek name for a pea or pulse. *Lathyrus* species are both annuals and perennials, and are usually climbing plants, grown for their beautiful flowers and fragrance. *Lathyrus hirsutus*, *L. sativus*, and *L. sylvestris* are grown for green manure and topsoil stabilisation. *L. sativus* is also used as a food crop in India, where it is known as 'grass pea'. *L. latifolius*, the perennial or everlasting sweet pea, is a great favourite in cottage gardens.

There are hundreds of varieties of sweet pea – from striped to tendril-free. But a purely yellow-flowered variety still eludes the enthusiast.

Wild progenitors, and many early varieties of the modern garden plants, remain extant, illustrating the story of selective breeding. The plant is easily crossed, giving rise to new varieties. The wild pea has scented, purple flowers and still grows on the shores of the Mediterranean, especially in Malta and parts of Sardinia.

Modern records of sweet pea cultivation began in 1695, when a Franciscan monk – Father Cupani – first noted a variety different from the wild flower in the monastery garden at Palermo, Sicily. Four years later, he supplied seeds to an Englishman, Dr Robert Uvedale, a teacher and collector of

were probably bicolour, with a maroon-purple standard and magenta purple wings.

The popularity of the sweet pea spread during the 18th century, and by 1800, five varieties were known, including the purple bicolour. There were a white, a maroon, a red, and a pink and white-flowered sweet pea, known as 'Painted Lady'. Painted Lady was one of the first varieties recorded, and is still available.

The person who did most to develop and popularise sweet peas was Henry Eckford, who was born in England in 1823. By the 20th century, almost 300 varieties were known, and Eckford was responsible for over 100 of them. He worked largely by trial and error, as the science of genetics was then in its infancy. He was responsible for shipping sweet pea varieties to America, where a great demand for Eckford varieties developed.

The sweet pea offered Victorian gardeners two great advantages: it responded well to good methods of cultivation, and was not greatly bothered by pests and diseases – both factors that helped establish its popularity. The sweet peas developed by Henry Eckford were generally larger-flowered than earlier varieties, and were termed 'grandifloras'. Today, they are commonly referred to as 'old-fashioned types', and are valued for their dainty, beautifully scented flowers, in a range of intense colours.

Around 1900, Silas Cole, the gardener at Althorp Park, Northamptonshire; Mr W. J. Unwin, a grocer in Histon, near Cambridge, and Mr E. Viner of Frome, all noticed a new 'waved edge' form of sweet pea in their gardens. These new sweet peas all appeared in rows of the variety 'Prima Donna', developed by Henry Eckford in 1896. All three gardeners gave names to their new

fully frilled edges. It was named 'Countess Spencer', after the Spencer family, and for this reason all modern forms of sweet pea are known as 'Spencer types'.

Spencer types have now largely superseded the old-fashioned types, showing almost infinite variation in size and degree of waviness or frilling, colour and fragrance. However, the fragrance of some of the old-fashioned types, preferred by some people, has been lost.

Sweet peas are easily grown. They need a well-drained garden soil, a sunny, open position, and some sort of support. They must be watered thoroughly in dry weather, and regular removal of the blooms actually encourages the plant to flower more. The flowering period, depending upon variety, is from June to October.

Our Making of Garden Flowers exhibit shows old and new varieties of sweet pea.

Two varieties of sweet pea. The purple flower is an old-fashioned variety – 'Cupani's 1699'. The white flower is a modern 'Spencer type', with a frilled edge.

sweet
pea

59

Even before dinosaurs roamed the Earth, ferns were well established. They are some of the oldest living plants in the world, and many are regarded as living fossils.

There are some 10,000 species of ferns and their allies – including clubmosses, quillworts and horsetails – distributed throughout the world, in nearly all ecological areas. Most are herbaceous, but a number develop a fibre of adventitious, above-ground roots at the base of the stem, and acquire the stature of simple trees.

The Australian soft tree fern – *Dicksonia antarctica* – is a species with this distinctive growth habit. The family Dicksoniaceae consists of about 25 species. *D. antarctica* is evergreen, and grows to a height of 9 m. (30 ft.), with fronds of up to 4.5 m. (15 ft.) in length. In the wild, it grows from sea level to altitudes of more than 1,000 m. (3,280 ft.) – typically in forested areas, favouring deep, shaded gullies, wet mountain slopes, or seepages near waterfalls and streams. It is native to the Australian provinces of New South Wales, Tasmania, and Victoria.

Tree ferns were a food source for the indigenous people of Australia. The pith in the upper part of the trunk, just below the growing point, is eaten raw or roasted, and is a source of starch. The young leaves – harvested just before they unfurl – can also be cooked. They are juicy and slimy in texture, and taste like bitter celery.

Today, the tree fern's primary use is as an ornamental, exotic landscape plant. *D. antarctica* was introduced into Britain in 1786, and into Cornish gardens from New South Wales in the late 19th century by John Treseder, a nurs-

Dicksonia antarctica is the hardiest tree fern in Britain. It has even established itself as a garden escape in some parts of Cornwall.

eryman from Truro, Cornwall, who travelled extensively in search of rare exotics that would survive in Britain's milder regions. Indeed, the Treseder family was renowned for its nursery, and for introducing many Australian hardy plants to Britain's gardens.

D. antarctica have been grown in Britain for more than 100 years, succeeding out of doors only in the milder parts. They are typically propagated from spores, sown at any time in a warm greenhouse and germinating after 1–3 months at 20°C. (68°F) *D. antarctica* thrive in cool, moist conditions, and tolerate snow, but not severe frosts. Recent collections imported from Tasmania are believed to be slightly more frost hardy, but this has yet to be proved.

Today, with a growing interest in tree ferns, mature specimens are rescued from Tasmanian forests under threat from logging. But occasionally, tree ferns are brought into this country from illegal sources. *D. antarctica* now appears on the Convention on International Trade in Endangered Species (CITES) list, and any tree ferns from Tasmanian forests must be imported under licence.

The Eden Project's *D. antarctica* are in the Flowerless Garden, their tree-like structures shading other non-flowering plants, including clubmosses and horsetails.

tree fern

1. and 2. Tree ferns flourish in cool, moist conditions.

Tree ferns have a very slow growth rate – only about 30 cm. (1 ft.) every ten years.

The willow belongs to the family Salicaceae – a small family of woody, flowering trees and shrubs, which includes poplars, aspens and cottonwoods. *Salix* – the Latin name for willow – derives from the Celtic *sallis* – 'near water'.

There are around 400 species of willow, and more than 200 listed hybrids. *Salix* are most numerous throughout the British Isles and Europe; Asia – especially China and Japan; North America, and Canada. Some 20 species are native to Britain. The white willow – *Salix alba* – is the most common. A fast-growing tree, it reaches 25 m. (82 ft.) in height, and can live for up to 120 years. It grows mainly in lowland woods, beside rivers, and tolerates prolonged spring floods. But perhaps the best known willow in Britain is the Pussy willow, or sallow, which is common in damp woods, and on heaths and rough ground. It grows to a maximum height of 10 m. (33 ft.), and lives for up to 60 years.

Willows produce male and female flowers on separate plants. The flowers, or catkins, are simple, and lack both sepals and petals. They appear in spring, before or during the growth of new leaves, and produce abundant, scented nectar that attracts insects – especially bees and moths – for pollination.

The stems are light, flexible and durable, and over the years have had a great many uses. The Celts made willow baskets, and passed on their skills to the Romans. Coracles – small boats of wickerwork covered with watertight material – were an early form of basketry, and are still used on some Welsh rivers.

Willow twigs, called 'osiers', are used to make baskets, lobster- and crab-pots and furniture. The three most important species for this purpose are the almond-leaved willow – *Salix triandra* – the purple osier – *Salix purpurea* – and the common osier – *Salix viminalis*. The biggest willow-growing area in Britain is around Taunton, in Somerset. In winter and early spring, the osier willows are coppiced – cut to ground level – to produce the long, straight, leafless rods used by craftspeople.

Today, a more important, specialised use of willow is the production of timber for the manufacture of cricket bats. The wood is obtained exclusively from *Salix alba* var. *coerulea*. It is tough, durable, light, springy, straight-grained and white. The cricket-bat industry is concentrated in East Anglia, using local willow. The trees are felled at around ten years old, when each one produces up to 32 bats.

A less well-known use of willow is in the manufacture of aspirin – probably the world's most widely used drug. Aspirin is a derivative of salicylic acid, which was first extracted from the bark and leaves of the white willow, *Salix alba*. Willow had long been used as a pain-killer, and in 1827, salicin – the compound responsible for pain-relief – was isolated. Today, salicylic acid is produced synthetically.

Of increasing importance is the use of willow as a biofuel. Compared with fossil fuels, wood is very economical: it produces heat rapidly; is clean-burning, and leaves very little ash. It is a good source of renewable energy. The carbon dioxide released when burned is less than that absorbed by the growing willow – an important factor in combating the production of greenhouse gases.

In early spring, before most other flowers appear, insects rely on the nectar of willow catkins as a food source.

You can see willows in the Eden Project's Wild Cornwall display, and in the Plants for Fuel exhibit, which looks at plants as alternatives to fossil fuels.

1. *Salix caprea*, pussy willow.
2. Ornamental willows are popular in gardens.
3. Coracles are still in use on some rivers in Wales and Ireland.
4. Lobster- and crab-pots are traditionally made from willow.
5. Cricket bats are made exclusively from *Salix alba* var. *coerulea*.

62

willow

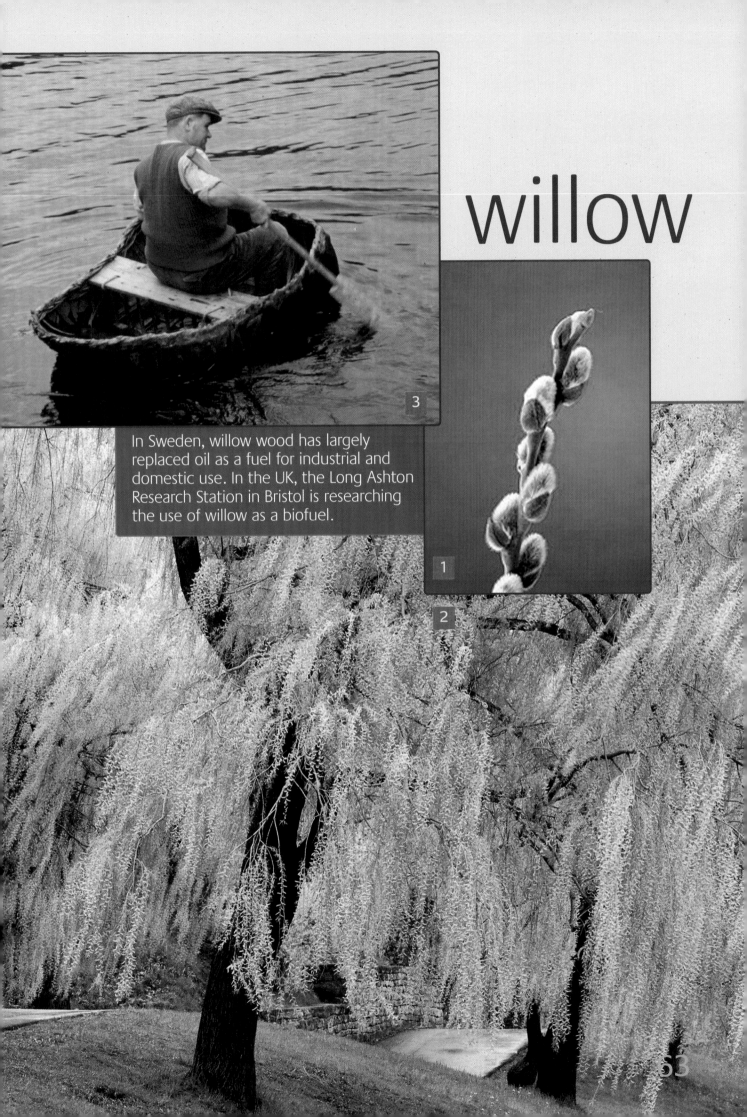

In Sweden, willow wood has largely replaced oil as a fuel for industrial and domestic use. In the UK, the Long Ashton Research Station in Bristol is researching the use of willow as a biofuel.

3

1

2

about the authors

Louise Frost

Louise Frost studied Biology at the University of Plymouth, and after specialising in the study of plants, obtained a degree in Plant Sciences. She is the Eden Project's Plant Records Manager. As part of the Science Team at Eden, her main role is to keep track of the thousands of plants, recording sources, locations, conditions, and flowering times on a botanical database. Louise writes regularly for the *Western Morning News*. This is her first book.

Alistair Griffiths

Alistair Griffiths left school at the age of 16 and trained at Myerscough Horticultural College for four years. He then took a degree in Botany at the University of Reading. A keen plantsman, Alistair is Assistant Scientific Officer and Plant Taxonomist at the Eden Project. He is about to undertake a PhD in genetic plant conservation of an endangered plant species from the Seychelles Islands. Alistair writes regularly for the *Western Morning News*. This is his first book.

acknowledgements

The authors would like to thank Dr Peter Whitbread-Abrutat and Dr Andrew Ormerod for reading early drafts of the manuscript.

Some of the chapters in this book are based on material previously published in the *Western Morning News*.

Photographs are reproduced by kind permission of: James L. Amos/CORBIS: p. 9 (2); Avon Rubber plc: p. 18 (4); Peter Barker/Panos Pictures: p. 21 (4, 5); Richard Bickel/ CORBIS: p. 24 (2); Deni Brown/Oxford Scientific Films: p. 12 (2); Pietro Cenini/Panos Pictures: p. 12 (3); Collections/ Michael StMaur Sheil: p. 62 (5); Martial Colomb/PhotoDisc: pp. 50–51 (3); Philippe Colombi/PhotoDisc: p. 51 (2); CORBIS: pp. 5 (3), 29 (1), 33 (2), 39 (2), 63 (2); Sue Cunningham/SCP: pp. 7 (2), 23 (4), 46–7 (2); Eden Project: p. 19 (2); Eden Project/Charles Francis: pp. 5 (1), 20 (1–3), 22–3 (1), 27 (1), 28–9 (3), 39 (orange), 45 (1), 47 (1), 56 (2); Eden Project/Ian Jackson, *Western Morning News*: pp. 17 (1), 43 (1), 49 (1), 59; Eden Project/Simon Burt: p. 13 (1); Flowers & Foliage: pp. 51 (1), 53 (1), cover; Owen Franken/CORBIS: p. 43 (2, 3); Michael Freeman/CORBIS: p. 19 (3); Lowell Georgia/CORBIS: p. 30 (4); Alison Hodge: inside front cover and title page, pp. 5 (2), 8–9 (1), 9 (4), 26 (3, 4), 27 (2), 30–31 (5), 34 (4), 35 (1, 2), 36 (4), 38 (3), 39 (1), 40–41 (1), 41 (4), 44 (4), 45 (2, 3), 61 (1, 2); James Hodge: pp. 62 (4), 63 (3); Christopher Laughton: pp. 16, 28–9 (background), 36 (3), 37 (2), 42 (5), 52 (3–5), 56–7 (3), 60; Museum of Kent Life: p. 49 (2); Charles O'Rear/ CORBIS: p. 29 (2); Gianni Dagli Orti/CORBIS: p. 7 (1); Panos Pictures/Betty Press: pp. 11 (2), 22 (2), 23 (3); PhotoDisc: pp. 14 (2, 3), 15 (1), 17 (2), 25 (1), 32–3 (1), 34 (3), 37 (1, 5), 38–9 (background), 41 (2, 3), 57 (1), 63 (1), PhotoDisc/ Kent Knudson: p. 31 (3); PhotoDisc/D. Normak: p. 17 (3); PhotoDisc/S. Solum, p. 31 (1, 2); Royal Botanic Garden, Edinburgh/Debbie White: pp. 54–5 (3), 55 (1, 2); St Austell Brewery, p. 48 (3); R. Sheridan/Ancient Art & Architecture Collection: p. 11 (3); John P. Stevens/Ancient Art & Architecture Collection: pp. 10–11 (1); Chris Stowers/Panos Pictures: p. 19 (1); Liba Taylor/Panos Pictures: p. 44 (5); United Distillers & Vintners: p. 6 (3); Wakefield Museums and Arts: p. 53 (2); W.T. Warren, St Just: p. 42 (4); Michael S. Yamashita/CORBIS: p. 9 (3).

First published in March 2001 by **Alison Hodge** Bosulval, Newmill, Penzance, Cornwall TR20 8XA.

Reprinted 2001 (twice).

Designed by **Christopher Laughton**.

ISBN 0 906720 29 X

British Library Cataloguing-in-Publication Data

A catalogue record for this book is available from the British Library.

Typeset by BDP – Book Development and Production, Penzance, Cornwall.

Cover photograph of *Strelitzia reginae* by Flowers & Foliage, Rachel Warne.

Printed on chlorine-free paper.

Printed and bound in the UK by St Ives (Roche) Ltd., St Austell, Cornwall.